THIS SIDE
THAT SIDE

'*This Side That Side: Restorying Partition* signals the coming of age of graphic novels in India'—JERRY PINTO

'my "most interesting book of 2013" ... a wistful playful potpourri of poetry, prose, comicstrip-lingua and graphic images fomented in imagination, nostalgia, dreams, pain, longing and laughter, recreating a historical event through memory and desire in a blaze of fresh tongues and hands. In stark black-and-white, there is something orphic about this experimental volume'—BRINDA BOSE, *BIBLIO*

'Our perception of the Partition lies, admittedly elusively, in a space where history has ended and the personal experience, often mediated by earlier generations in the family, has taken over. Textbooks cannot take us there, but art certainly can. And *This Side, That Side* does that effectively.... By dint of sheer variety, interleaved with tales of the unexpected, uncanny and untold, the collection proves that there are so many other sides besides the "this" and the "that" to this never-ending story'—ARUNAVA SINHA

'Tales of Partition have come to us in many forms, passed on from one generation to another, but none like in this, where art, photography and text freely mingle to tell stories'—*TIMEOUT DELHI*

'An original attempt at re-telling the story of the Partition ... a rather astonishing diversity of tales and sensibilities ... on the themes of separation, anomie, alienation and reconciliation on a grand scale'—*DHAKA TRIBUNE*

'... a valuable conversation about shared pasts and possible futures, a collection of illustrated memoirs and artistic commentary to help us understand the roots of our petty nationalisms, and to transcend them'—*THE CARAVAN*

'... dotted with delightful details and imaginations where memory has faded.... The book is a map, inviting the reader to situate themselves amid the three partitioned zones, and triangulate between them, until the triangle becomes a prism through which a singular light refracts into its parts, inseparable and infinite'—*TEHELKA*

'*This Side That Side* is not your average graphic novel; it's dreamy, mixing fantasy with reality and packed with humour and symbols that are open to interpretation'—*MIDDAY*

'A valuable read'—*LIVEMINT*

'*This Side, That Side*'s putting into pictures what has been knowable to post-midnight's children only in words can be seen as the book's greatest success.... an ambitious and innovative production'—*KITAAB*

'... unique because it looks at Partition not as political history but as personal histories; not as incidents that happened on the ground but as events that happened to individuals. Unique personal experiences cannot be circumscribed by dates on a historical calendar—because they continue to occur, continue to define lives even now'—*DAWN*

'The surrogate storytellers of *This Side That Side* are able to do what few have been able to do before: to treat the subject of "partition" with wit and dry humour, to be respectful to their text and still retain the colour of an imaginative rendering ... a brave and valiant effort'—*DOMUS*

'a melange of reflective, witty and contemporary accounts of how ordinary people negotiated with the Partition.... The anthology attempts to look beyond what has already been written about Partition since 1947'—*HINDUSTAN TIMES*

'Stories about Partition are plenty, but they have never been seen from the lens of the times we live in.... *This Side That Side* ... lends voices to young, unheard stories from the Indian subcontinent and sees the event from their eyes'—*FIRSTPOST*

'... undoubtedly an important book for it reminds us that, to borrow a line from the book, "This is not how nations are made."'—*DNA*

THIS SIDE
ƎᗡIƧ TAHT

RESTORYING PARTITION

*{graphic narratives
from Pakistan, India, Bangladesh}*

Curated by
VISHWAJYOTI GHOSH

YODA PRESS

 YODA PRESS
268 A/C Vasant Kunj
New Delhi 110 070
www.yodapress.in

In partnership with

**GOETHE
INSTITUT
MAX MUELLER
BHAVAN**

ISBN 978-93-82579-01-4

Editor in charge: Nishtha Vadehra
Design: invertedcommasindia@yahoo.com
Printed at Thomson Press (India) Ltd., New Delhi 110 020
Published by Arpita Das for YODA PRESS

CONTENTS

After years of dreams, debates and demands, it was time for the inevitable—the deadline. According to local witnesses who had followed the proceedings with great interest, it was the darkest monsoon cloud that arrived right before the summer. According to reports, rumours and reliable sources it was two, no three, no two-and-a-half months that one had, to get the job done. Long after the battle lines had been drawn, it was time to draw real lines. And soon the mapmakers arrived, armed with permanent markers with the power to seal the fate of millions, if not more. But they had other plans. The exercise had to be executed in the right spirit of democracy, an institution they had set up back home. It was time to hand over.

Soon, the black markers travelled across the region, into the hands of the masses and the millions. The brief was simple—make your own map. Democracy prevailed. This would be fun, they said. Drawing personal territories of nationhood—a beautiful post-dinner exercise, good for digestion. It was time to dream again, draw castles and settle scores. There could be no greater joy than marking one's territory on the lines of faith, freedom and personal convenience. The masses smiled as they smelt power—as addictive as the scent of the marker. For days they would sniff the black, plastic marker that clearly said 'Recap after use'. A few bothered to think about the exercise and pondered over the chart paper that came with the disclaimer: 'Nation-making in progress. Inconvenience is not regretted'. No sooner had they commited pen to paper, they realised their game was up. The marker was dry. They had either left it open too long or it was permanently dry. The power to draw had passed the expiry date. A missed, no, a lost opportunity that never really mattered to begin with. The opinion of the people was not really important and they would now have to live in nations marked by the opium of the people. After all, deadlines had to be honoured.

After geographical decisions by consultation and committees were sealed, the next rollout was unanimously arrived on. After the marker fiasco, all parties were of the opinion that the rollout must be such that people are only told and never asked for opinions. Soon tin trunks reached all houses along with cyclostyled maps for your information. More important than a You-are-here, each came with the poser: Are-you-sure-you-are-here? Such pervasive planning by the planners-that-be! Formula'47 was now hardwired into the collective psyche that would remain for generations to come. The formula had three simple words: Is life elsewhere? Whether or not one was changing sides, the key was to wonder: What if I move? What is left for me here? What is it like on the other side? Now the tin trunks had a two-in-one purpose in a land that was divided one-by-two and then three. One, the masses were busy packing up their futures across borders and, in many ways, they are still at it. Two, research reveals that this metal lasts long enough for each trunk to become an eternal memory box. Now and then, letters and photographs fly out of them, scanned and colour-corrected, posted on blogs and such projects of memory seeking a connection with the other side. Airbrushed memories can be safer than making calls, where the service provider reminds you, asks you and tells you 'this an international call'. Visit if you must, but with Form C, D or Z that takes you to the local police station, -to announce the arrival of a Foreigner. How you became them and them the other is a story that keeps changing currency at every checkpost, reminding one of the lessons in those letter-pressed textbooks in school. Using the same footage, history keeps changing its story at every border. The results of a subcontinental Rashomon effect, now packed in brown paper covers, that must be mugged up for the next school function and forever. The learnings of one's impressionable years now manifest themselves in the exuberance of a cricket stadium. Floodlit nationalism now sponsored by a soft drink that is available in all three countries. The nights look younger now than those evenings of listening to the same old grandiose stories told by grandparents. Those fictions are now photo-framed installations of memory. At the same time, memory too was partitioned, long before the invention of memory cards. Indus Valley Civilisation, 1947, 1971 are the convenient markers of beginnings. Collective mapmaking must only begin from then on.

Restorying Partition can never be easy. If one wants to avoid the usual revival of Mass Memory, one has to look beyond those maps lodged in our nervous systems that make nervous headlines on our televisions. To listen to the subsequent generations and the grandchildren and how they have negotiated maps that never got drawn. *This Side, That Side* is a tiny drop in the river of stories that must be told before the markers run dry.

This is a book I had once planned to write but didn't manage to. And so, when I was offered this honourable task, I smelt the scent of the black marker. By soliciting contributions I looked for help to chase a dream to its logical end, through us, them and the others. An open call-for-contributions was the first step; many of the responses find themselves in the pages of this book. Stories I had bothered to remember over chai and beer came next. Frantic emails and calls, cajoling and massaging of egos followed, till the point where it said 'line busy'. Many of those narratives arrived, most didn't. Beautiful stories in the long form were dropped, with the hope that one will read them again somewhere. Poets, filmmakers, musicians and a range of fresh voices were chased, including those who remained unsure of how their stories would look visually, how they would find life in print. Many took up the challenge to find themselves here. Online collaborations between like-minded souls who have never met were fruitful across borders.

From the tin trunk of memories, *This Side, That Side* hopes to open the cabinets of curiosities that exist on all sides, with markers that must be recapped after use. This is not a closure, but one of many beginnings.

Vishwajyoti Ghosh,
New Delhi.

ACKNOWLEDGEMENTS

Thank you is an understatement when it comes to all the contributors of this anthology, many of whom extended themselves beyond their familiar disciplines of practice, many who delivered stories within tight or impossible timelines. I am grateful to everyone who responded to the open call and helped widen the canvas.

Our acknowledgements are due to Farah Batool, Robin Mallick and Goethe Institut, Delhi, for their prompt response and support to what was in the beginning just an idea. Without their support, the project would have remained just that, a great idea. To Judith Mirschberger, Tanvir Alim, Dr Manuel Negwer, Kashif Paracha, Dr Martin Wälde and Sharmistha Sarker of the Goethe Institut, a big thank you for all the help and support.

My thanks to Aijaz Hussain, Syeda Farhana, Jaya Bhattacharji Rose, Ahmad Rafay Alam, Indrajit Hazra, Anusha Rizvi, Musharraf A Farooqi, Jai Arjun Singh, Iqbal Geoffrey, Ashwani Kumar, Abdul Malik Channa, Priya Kuriyan, Tabish Khair, Muzzumil Ruheel, Kaushik Ramaswamy, Naresh Fernandes, Indira Kumar, Haider Ali Jaan, Abeer Hoque, Amitabh Kumar, Mohammed Hanif, Nitin K Pamnani, Shveta Sarda and Pinaki De for important leads and introductions. Much of your enthusiasm and help finds itself here.

Importantly, to the guardian angels of Yoda Press, Arpita Das, for those sessions, coffee and enthusiasm; Nishtha Vadehra, for the handholding, the long nights of edits, and taking care of logistics and emails of all sorts; to Dharmender Kandwal, for his perseverance and support. To Rajinder Singh for his endless patience and long hours on the system, page by page, frame by frame.

And finally, The Family, Indrani Sen for her patience and for understanding the complications of a restorying exercise of this nature, and most importantly, to Aditri Sen Ghosh, for her unconditional love despite my erratic spells of absence during this project.

TABISH KHAIR

is an Indian writer, born and educated in Gaya, Bihar. Winner of the All India Poetry Prize, his four novels have also been shortlisted for various international and national awards, including the Man Asian Literary Prize. His new novel is titled *How to Fight Islamist Terror from the Missionary Position.*

Khair currently lives in Aarhus, Denmark.

PRIYA KURIYAN

Born in Cochin, she spent her childhood in numerous small cantonment towns in India. A graduate of the National Institute of Design, Ahmedabad, she has directed educational films for the *Sesame Street Show,* India *(Galli Galli Sim Sim)* and has also co-directed a short animation film for the Children's Film Society of India. Over the past five years she has illustrated a number of children's books and comics, the last one being *When Ali became Bajrangbali* (Tulika Books).

She currently lives and works in Delhi.

AN OLD FABLE

His courtiers hailed him for being the One who had brought Reason to the country, and Law too.

I want a Law too! I want a Law too!

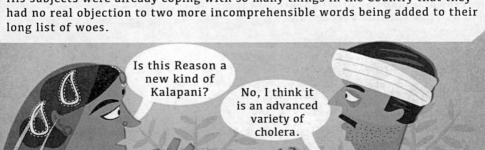

His subjects were already coping with so many things in the Country that they had no real objection to two more incomprehensible words being added to their long list of woes.

Is this Reason a new kind of Kalapani?

No, I think it is an advanced variety of cholera.

But one day two women rushed to his court, carrying a newborn baby.

The woman in green claimed that the child was hers.

No, actually, the women did not say much. It was the crowd around each that shouted on their behalf. They shouted very loudly.

The woman in saffron
claimed that the child
was hers.

They shouted so loudly that the King jumped off his throne. He
ordered ear-plugs to be brought. After he had plugged his ears, he
turned to them and said:

OK, little buggers. Go
ahead. What's troubling
your dense heads? I am
here to listen.

The King's courtiers interpreted for the King. They wrote down the crowd's complaints in convoluted petitions full of legalese.

The gist of the petitions did not generally tally.

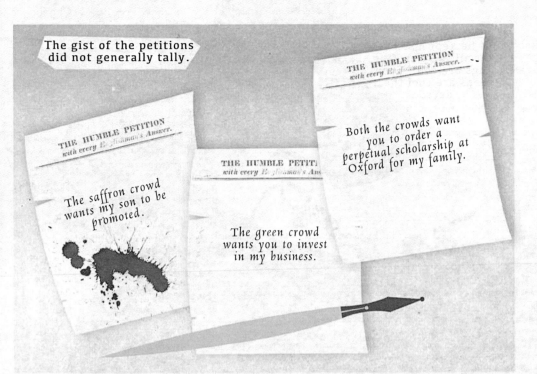

THE HUMBLE PETITION
with every Englishman's Answer.

Both the crowds want you to order a perpetual scholarship at Oxford for my family.

THE HUMBLE PETITION
with every Englishman's Answer.

The saffron crowd wants my son to be promoted.

THE HUMBLE PETITI
with every E

The green crowd wants you to invest in my business.

But gradually, the King got a rough notion of the problem.

He had a problem too.

Ahhhh. Both these women are claiming the child for their own! How bloody unreasonable!

Two women having a baby together! It's illogical. It's unscientific! It's unnatural! It's illegal! It's... it's impossible.

But he kept his cool. After all, he was King. Kings are cool. Even Queens are cool these days.

He ordered the child to be brought closer to him.

23

Then he returned to the audience and issued his wise judgement.

We hereby announce that in the name of Reason, Science and, above all, Law and Order, this newborn, stinking, undiapered child should be cut in half, and each half given to each of the disputing mothers.

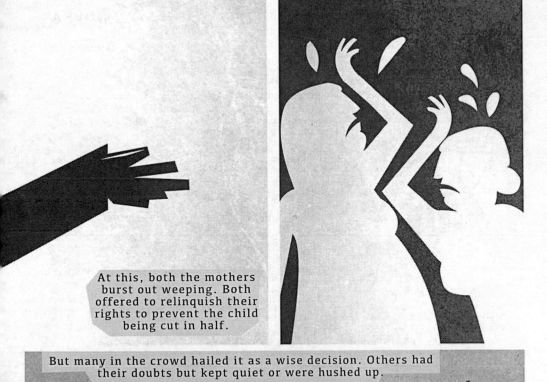

At this, both the mothers burst out weeping. Both offered to relinquish their rights to prevent the child being cut in half.

But many in the crowd hailed it as a wise decision. Others had their doubts but kept quiet or were hushed up.

Actually, everyone except a very old and frail man in loincloth, who was politely ignored.

Shut up, grandpa!

Grandpa, go home!

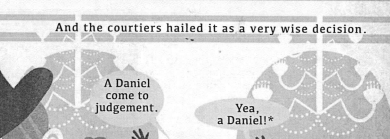

But then a problem arose. It was a merely technical problem. Should the baby be parted horizontally or vertically?

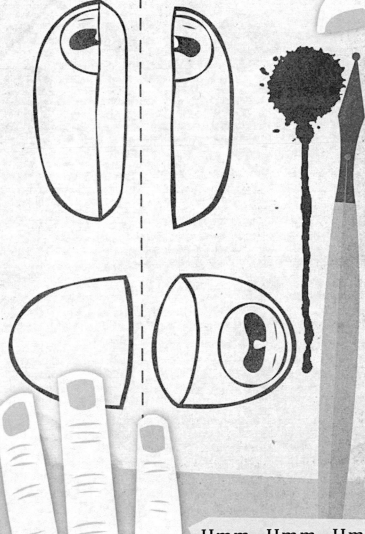

Hmm. Hmm. Hmmmm.

And that is how, as we know from our old-old stories, the newborn baby was divided into three parts, and everyone (except the baby) lived unhappily ever after.

The King when he retired, which he did very soon after this historic verdict, could record in his memoirs, published by Faber and Faber or Bloomsbury (we get confused between the two) in England, and translated into 47 languages:

We always knew that two women could not have a baby together. We always said so. It stands to Reason. And that's how it happened.

End

IRFAN MASTER

is the author of *A Beautiful Lie* (his debut novel), published
by Bloomsbury, shortlisted for the Waterstone's Children's Book
Prize and the Branford Boase Award, and translated into seven
languages. Irfan is currently working with the charity, First Story
as a writer in residence. Recently, he has been working on a
commissioned story to be produced as a stage show, and his second
novel will be published shortly. Irfan has contributed poetry and
short stories to various anthologies. He regularly speaks about the
creative writing process to young people and adults.

Irfan lives and works in Leicester, UK.

PRABHA MALLYA

is an illustrator, writer and comic book maker.
She is at her happiest fussing around with stubby pencils
and black inks, and frequently has black fingernails.
She has illustrated for *Beastly Tales from Here and There*,
The *Wildings* and *The F-Word,* and several book covers.
Her graphic short stories have appeared in *Mint, Forbes Life*
and *Brainwave* magazine.

She lives in Stanford, California.

FAULT LINES

SWEEP
SWEEP

35

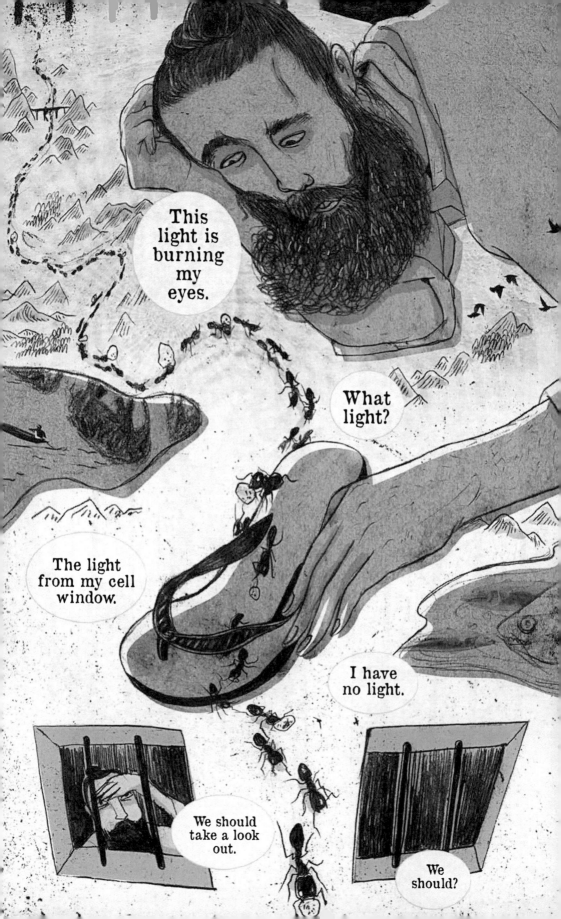

"SOMETHING TERRIFIC WILL COME NO MATTER HOW DARK THE PRESENT."

— Rabindranath Tagore

fin

KAISER HAQ

is a poet, essayist and translator, and Professor
of English at Dhaka University (on leave) and the
University of Liberal Arts Bangladesh. He has to his
credit seven volumes of poetry, the most recent being
Published in the Streets of Dhaka: Collected Poems
(UPL 2012), five translated books and two edited
poetry anthologies.

He currently lives in Dhaka.

HEMANT PURI

Academically a painter, he has worked a retail designer/visual
merchandiser for some of the best brands, and writes in English,
Hindi and Urdu. Currently he works as an artist using different
media including performance and sound. He is an avid learner of
dhrupad music.

He lives in New Delhi.

BORDER

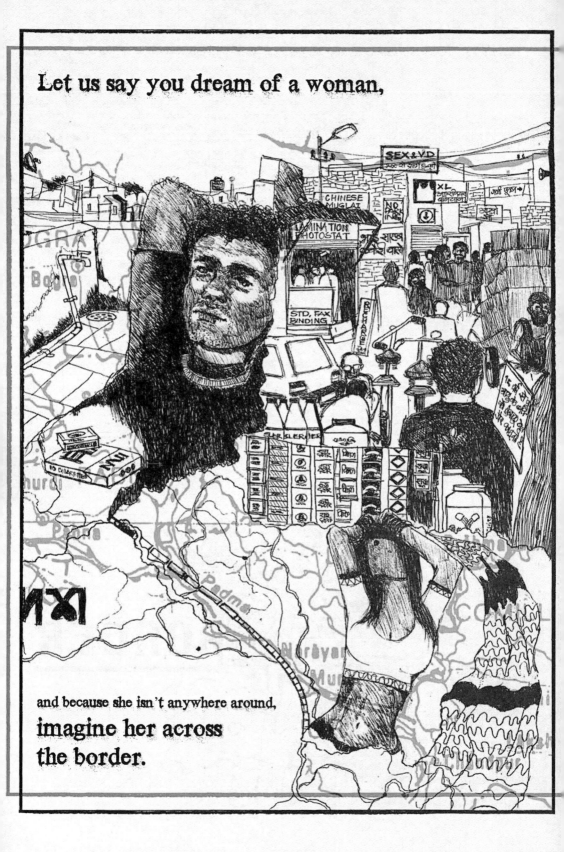

You travel hunched and twisted
in a crowded bus,
on a ferry through the opaque night
lacerated by searchlights,

to this squalid frontier town:

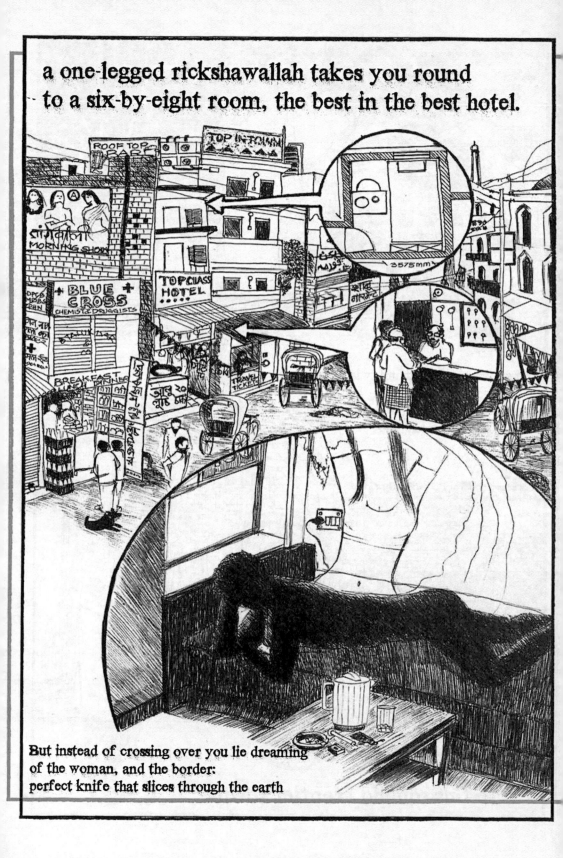

a one-legged rickshawallah takes you round
to a six-by-eight room, the best in the best hotel.

But instead of crossing over you lie dreaming
of the woman, and the border:
perfect knife that slices through the earth

without the earth's knowing,
severs and joins at the same instant,

runs inconspicuously through modest households,

creating wry humour—whole families
eat under one flag, shit under another,

humming a different national tune.

You lie down on the fateful line
under a livid moon. You
and your desire and the border are now one.

You raise the universal flag
of flaglessness. Amidst bird anthems
dawn explodes in a lusty salute.

End

RAVISH KUMAR

is a blogger and a story writer besides being a news anchor and reporter with NDTV, popular for his show 'Ravish ki Report'. A recent winner of the Ramnath Goenka Award, he is also a lover of history.

He lives and works in Delhi.

IKROOP SANDHU

is constantly seeking something of an undiscovered nature.
She freelances as an animator primarily for Raqs Media Collective.
Her illustrated work has appeared in *Pao Anthology of Comics* and *The Mint*. She is currently working on 'Bombay Velvet', a graphic novel by Gyan Prakash.

She lives in Dharamsala and is preparing the soil for her roots to grow.

SHVETA SARDA

is an editor and translator based in Delhi. During her tenure at Sarai, she worked on *Galiyon Se/by lanes*, *Book Box*, the blog 'Nangla's Delhi', *No Apologies for the Interruption, Bahurupiya Shehr* (Rajkamal Prakashan, 2007), and *Trickster City* (Penguin, 2010). She co-edited, with Nikolaus Hirsch, *Cybermohalla Hub* (Sternberg/Berlin, 2012) and with Raqs Media Collective, *Sarai Reader 09: Projections* (Sarai-CSDS, 2013). She was Associate Curator for 'Sarai Reader 09: The Exhibition' (curated by Raqs Media Collective, 2012–13, at the Devi Art Foundation, Gurgaon).
She is currently translating two novels by Bhisham Sahni.

WHICH SIDE?

{Translated from Hindi by Shveta Sarda}

{*LAPREK (लप्रेक)* is an acronym for Laghu Prem Katha, a short love story, a kind of micro-fiction that can fit into one's Facebook status.
In his stories, Ravish tries to sketch the urban spaces of non-Lutyen's Delhi.}

Turning their backs to the nights of Jinnah and Jawahar's negotiations,

they locked their gaze
into the Yamuna coursing
behind the Old Fort.

'That can't be how nations are made.'

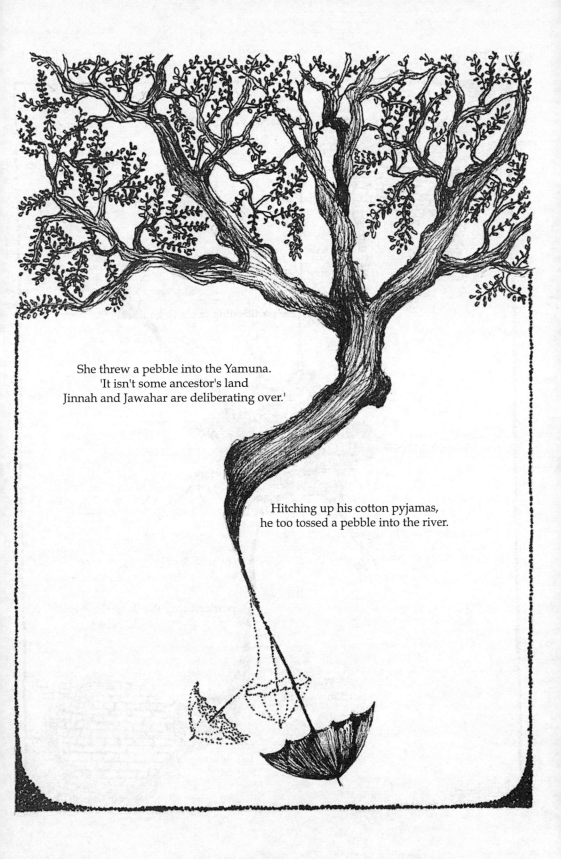

She threw a pebble into the Yamuna.
'It isn't some ancestor's land
Jinnah and Jawahar are deliberating over.'

Hitching up his cotton pyjamas,
he too tossed a pebble into the river.

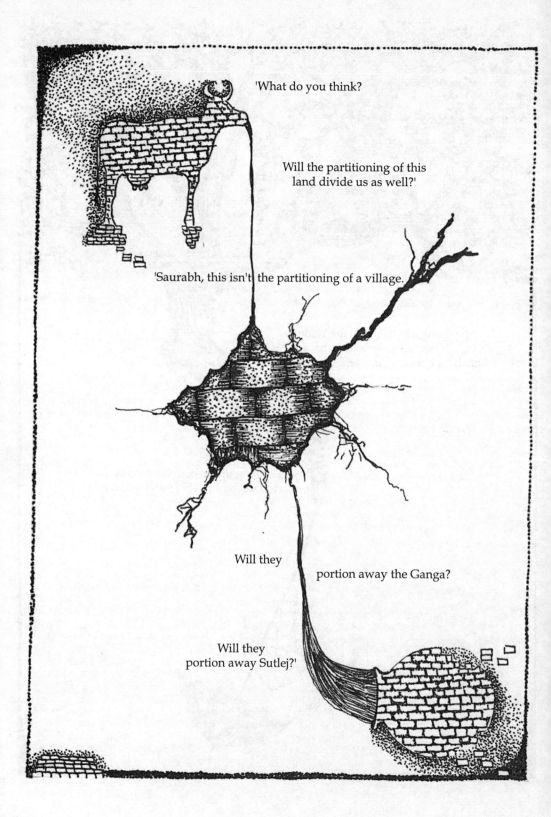

'What do you think?

Will the partitioning of this
land divide us as well?'

'Saurabh, this isn't the partitioning of a village.

Will they

portion away the Ganga?

Will they
portion away Sutlej?'

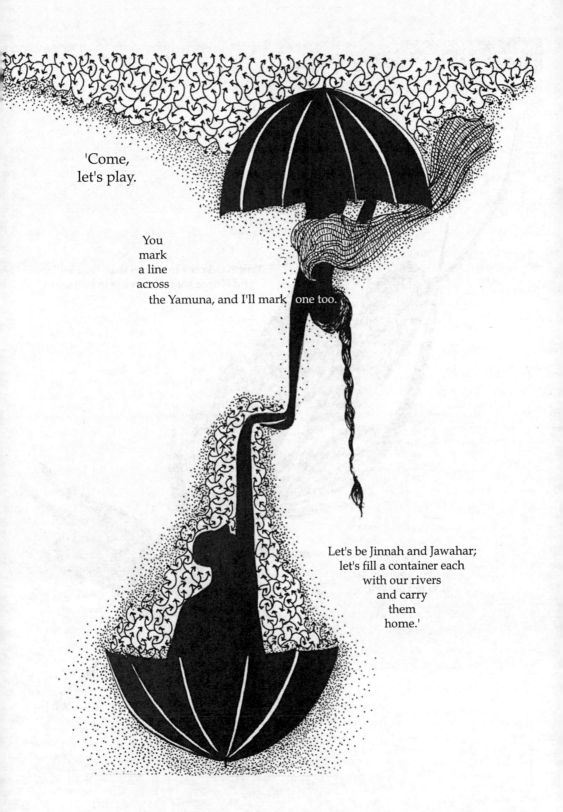

'Come,
let's play.

You
mark
a line
across
the Yamuna, and I'll mark one too.

Let's be Jinnah and Jawahar;
let's fill a container each
with our rivers
and carry
them
home.'

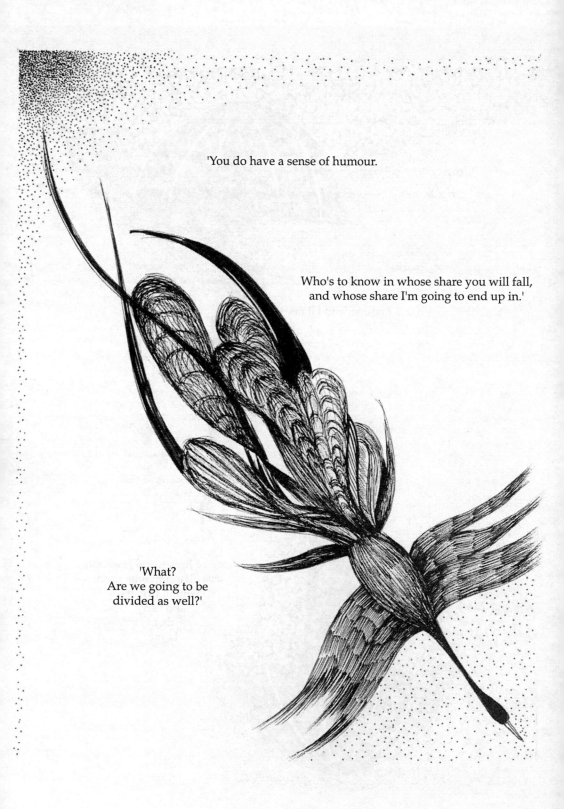

'You do have a sense of humour.

Who's to know in whose share you will fall,
and whose share I'm going to end up in.'

'What?
Are we going to be
divided as well?'

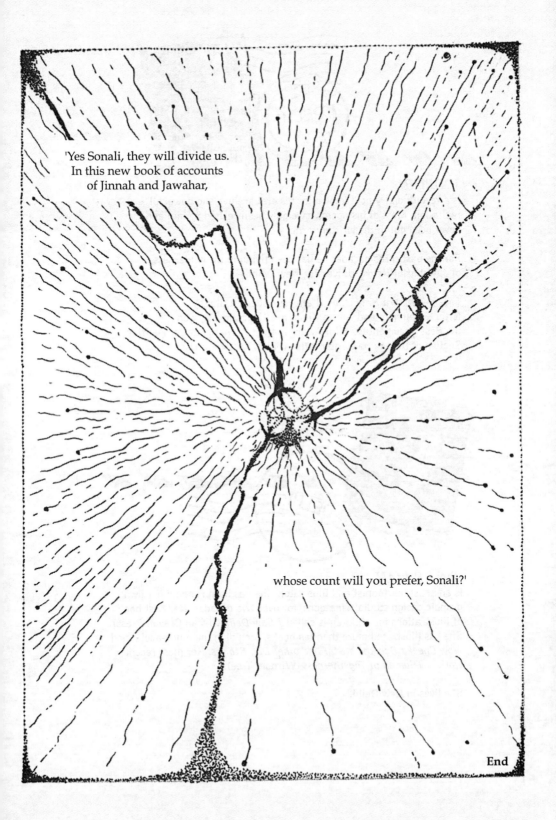

'Yes Sonali, they will divide us. In this new book of accounts of Jinnah and Jawahar,

whose count will you prefer, Sonali?'

End

VIDROHI

is a revolutionary poet known for his oral archive and powerful recitation. Most of his poems have only been recited by him and never been put in the written form.

For the past three decades he has been living in the wilderness of Jawaharlal Nehru University, New Delhi.

{ *Main Tumhara Kavi Hoon* (I am your poet), a film by Nitin K Pamnani and Imran Khan, based on Vidrohi, won the Best Documentary Film Award in the International Competition Section of the Mumbai International Film Festival 2012.}

TINA RAJAN

is an artist, cartoonist and illustrator. She has been running her own graphic design studio, Tinatoons, for over two decades. Her first book of illustrations for children is called *I Saw Delhi* (Urban Crayon Press). She has illustrated more than ten books, including the much-acclaimed *How Cheeka Became a Star and other Dog Stories.* Her most recent work is *Triumph of Togetherness* (Wisdom Tree).

She lives in New Delhi.

NOOR MIYAN

{Translated from Hindi by Shveta Sarda}

Today some may line their eyes with Victoria kohl
Even as others choose Sadhvi Rithambara's eyewash
But that surma perfected with pure cow's ghee
Was made by the one and only Noor miyan.

Daadi, look he's here!

Madam ji, this is the best kohl!

Noor miyan, you're too expensive!

Well, my grandmother swore by it.
Whenever Noor miyan came by,
My grandmother was sure to buy from him.

Lined with that surma, the old woman's eyes
Would surge like rain clouds,
And dance like the rivers Ganga and Yamuna,
They would become infinite oceans
In which we children could behold
Our entire world.

My grandmother would call blessings
On Noor miyan and his surma.

She'd say, it's thanks only to
Noor miyan's surma that
I roam about like a young girl
in this old age,
I can still thread needles.

You need help with this?

Shh...
I am still young

Daadi,
when will you
grow up?

And I'd want to say —
O old lady!
You're the beautiful princess Sukanya,
and Noor miyan your sage Chyawan*

* In the Mahabharata version of the story, the young princess Sukanya was given in marriage by her father to the aged sage, Chyawan, after she poked the sage's eyes by mistake, thereby enraging him. When the Ashwin brothers—the doctors of the gods, the devas of Ayurveda—tried to seduce her away from him, she refused and, instead, made them use their knowledge to heal his eyes and rejuvenate him physically.

And his surma is Chyawanprash*,
the life-herb that revitalises your eyes.
Your eyes are not just eyes, they are the divine
And that surma, an offering made by Noor miyan.

This was Noor miyan, and then he went away to Pakistan.

*Also the name of a popular health supplement today, Chyawanprash is referred to in the Mahabharata as the herbal elixir prepared for sage Chyawan by the Ashwin brothers. Food specially prepared (*prash*) for sage Chyawan, hence *Chyawanprash*.

Why did Noor miyan have to leave for Pakistan?
They say there was nothing to hold him here.
Does that mean we were no one to him?
Why did Noor miyan go to Pakistan
Without a word to us,
A goodbye to my grandmother?

Why did Noor miyan leave us for Pakistan?

After that, neither the surma remained, nor those eyes.
My grandmother returned
To where she'd come from.

She had married here from across the river,
And across the river is where we cremated her.

As I scattered her ashes
into the river, I felt,
This river is no longer a river
but has turned into her eyes
And the ashes in my hand
are the surma that will line those eyes.

And in this way, for one last time,
I applied Noor miyan's surma to my grandmother's eyes.

End

MAHMOOD FAROOQUI

effected the revival of Dastangoi, the art of Urdu storytelling,
and co-directed the highly acclaimed Hindi feature film *Peepli Live*
with Anusha Rizvi. His first book, *Besieged: Voices from Delhi 1857*
was hailed as a brilliant contribution to 1857 studies and recently
won the Ramnath Goenka Award. His translation of *Habib Tanvir:
Memoirs* was recently released.

He lives and works in Delhi.

FARIHA REHMAN

is an artist and art teacher. She has worked as Curator at Nairang Gallery, Lahore,
and has taught miniature painting and drawing at the Hunerkada College of Visual
and Performing Arts, Lahore. She was the assistant curator with Nayyar Ali Dada
for 'Representing Pakistan', a group show at Lalit Kala Academy Art Gallery, New
Delhi, in 2004. She is an independent miniature artist and her works have been
shown at several national and international exhibitions. Her work deals with issues
of womanhood and the juxtaposition of female form in South Asian culture.

She lives and works in Lahore.

{*DASTANGOI* is the art of Urdu storytelling where the performer
often improvises on the stories he tells. The last great Dastango,
Mir Baqar Ali passed away in 1928. Following the scholarship of
SR Faruqi, the form has seen a major revival in the last decade
under Mahmood Farooqui, Danish Husain, Anusha Rizvi and a team
of Dastangos. Their repertoire includes a mix of traditional
stories of adventure and sorcery, and more contemporary stories
like the 'Dastan-e Sedition' and 'Mantoiyat'.}

A LETTER
FROM INDIA

{Translated from Urdu by Mahmood Farooqui}

This segment is taken from the *Dastan-e Taqseem-e Hind,*
a collage of writings about Partition. It is from a short
story by Intizar Hussain called 'Hindustan se Ek Khat'.

listeners, watchers, gatherers,
benefactors and patrons,
if you want wisdom, go to the godmen,
if you want sex, crime, cinema, go watch the news,
if you want money, fame and success, go start a business.

we deal in truths
and true stories are hard to come by...
so here, we now present to you a story
that is not only true but happened
to my friend here, right now,
in this very year, on this very earth,
under this sun.

so, i am from ghazipur and a large part
of my family migrated to pakistan at the
time of partition, and like it happened
with many of you who came from pakistan
to india, a lot of things were left behind.
what was left behind of my family was a
brother of that generation who remained in
the village with his wife.

and when i recently went back to his village i found a bundle of crumbling letters in a dilapidated house. they were exchanges between him and his nephew who lived in karachi. here is one such letter written twenty-five years after partition, when pakistan itself had been partitioned into bangladesh and pakistan...

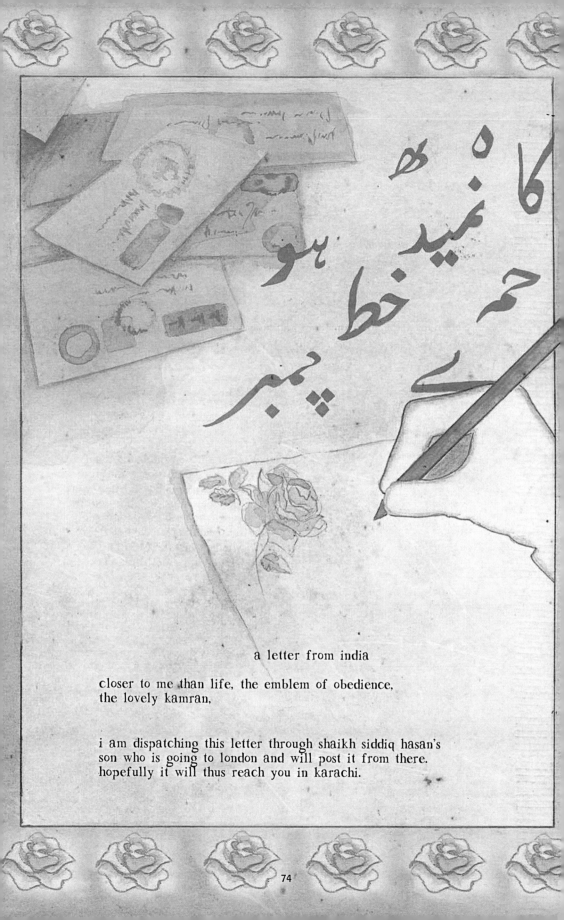

a letter from india

closer to me than life, the emblem of obedience,
the lovely kamran,

i am dispatching this letter through shaikh siddiq hasan's
son who is going to london and will post it from there.
hopefully it will thus reach you in karachi.

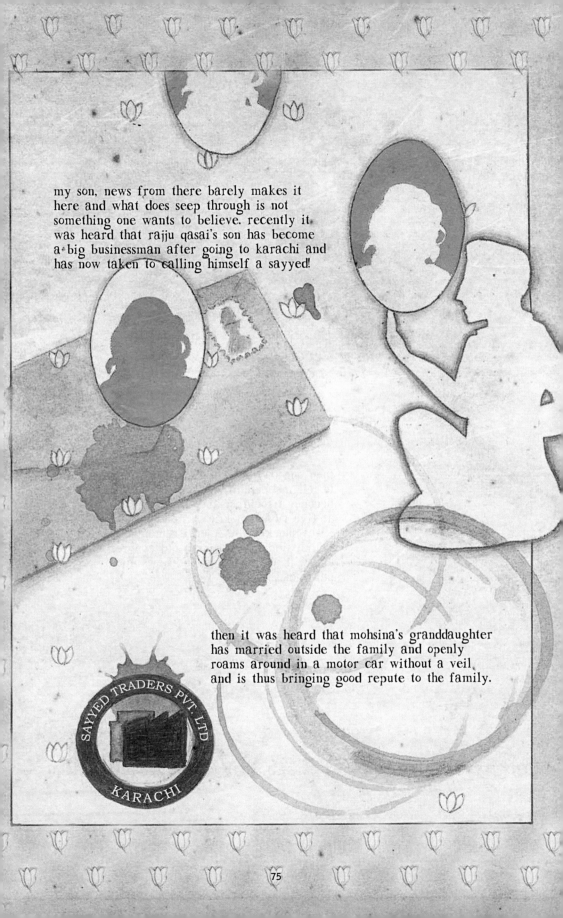

my son, news from there barely makes it here and what does seep through is not something one wants to believe. recently it was heard that rajju qasai's son has become a big businessman after going to karachi and has now taken to calling himself a sayyed!

then it was heard that mohsina's granddaughter has married outside the family and openly roams around in a motor car without a veil and is thus bringing good repute to the family.

SAYYED TRADERS PVT. LTD
KARACHI

then one day shaikh siddiq hasan came running
to tell me that in pakistan everybody has
become a socialist and that onions are selling
at five rupees a kilo.
i was shocked. but then i remembered that
shaikh siddiq hasan is an old congresswala
and will always bring bad news about
pakistan....

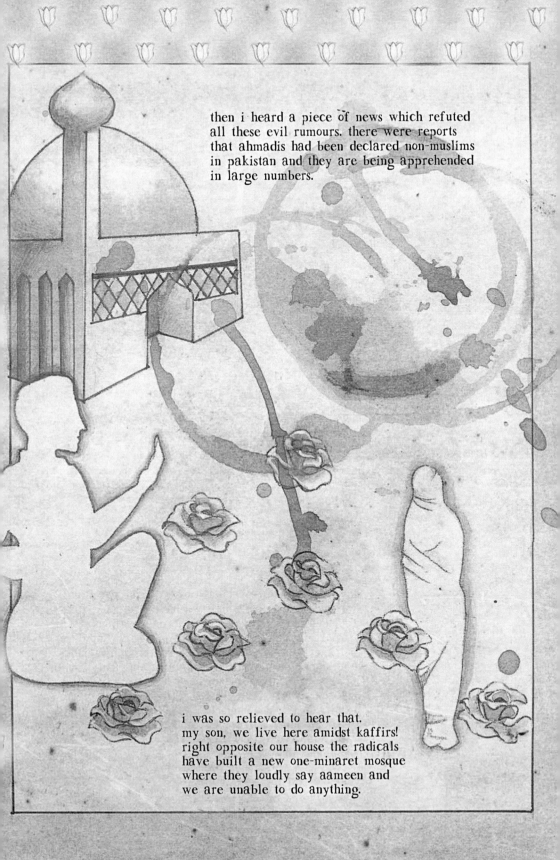

then i heard a piece of news which refuted all these evil rumours. there were reports that ahmadis had been declared non-muslims in pakistan and they are being apprehended in large numbers.

i was so relieved to hear that.
my son, we live here amidst kaffirs!
right opposite our house the radicals
have built a new one-minaret mosque
where they loudly say aameen and
we are unable to do anything.

my son, the most precious possession of our family
was our genealogy which we have protected for
fourteen hundred years but the depredations
of partitions snatched it out of our hands. now this
heirloom can only be transferred through memory,
and since you are the custodian of this family i am
sending you this information. i have collected the
figures. pyaare mian was the first member of our
family to lay down his life as a gift to the partition
of the country. since then thirty-one members of our
family have passed away. seven of them were killed
by hindus in india while fourteen were dispatched
to heaven by their muslim brethren in pakistan,
and the rest died naturally.

my son, it has been observed once the straws have scattered they never form a nest again, that when families disintegrate they rarely unite again. but a man must strive and make an effort. now that it is again possible to travel back and forth you must try and visit us and show us your face.

your aunt says you must not come alone, you must bring our daughter-in-law and your children. this way we will at least be able to observe your children and see which one is fair and who is dark.

my son, i am now a lonely mourner of leaves
that have been blown away. what else should
i say. consider this brief epistle to be a long one.
send news of your well being and tell me when
you are coming. i have seen and witnessed a lot
in this earthly life.
i have seen that too which should not be seen.
now i really only want to see that which
i have wanted to see all my life,

your far-flung chacha,
qurban ali

i read this letter and decided to get in touch with my relatives
whose names we have forgotten—our aunts, uncles, brothers, sisters
now lost to us. so i traced the number and made the call.
i did not get through after calling many times but i did get
a message from my phone company:
'you called a number with the code 0092----------.
you must be careful when calling any number with this code.
are you sure you want to call this code?'

i never called again.

end

KHADEMUL ISLAM

is concurrently literary editor of the *Dhaka Tribune* and editor of *Bengal Lights,* a literary journal. He is a short story writer, translator and critic, and has edited a book of short stories. He is writing a non-fiction book about escaping from Pakistan in the aftermath of the Bangladesh war of independence in 1971.

He lives, works and commutes between Dhaka and Bangkok.

SARBAJIT SEN

is a cartoonist/ graphic novelist/ filmmaker.

He currently lives in Kolkata.

THE EXIT PLAN

16 DECEMBER 1971
SOMEWHERE IN FREEZING KARACHI

...ALLIED FORCES OF BANGLADESH AND INDIA...

WHAT'S UP, MA?

TURN IT OFF. IT'S TOO LOUD.

SOMETHING IMPORTANT?

HMM.... QUITE IMPORTANT FOR ALL OF US.

AND MUM'S THE WORD.

OH! SO IT'S SECRET TOO! WELL, WHAT IS IT?

BACK TO BBC AGAIN

... AND THAT IS THE END OF THE NEWS TONIGHT.

GREAT! AND WHAT A PITY WE CANNOT EVEN CELEBRATE HERE!

DINNER READY?

ONLY IF YOU WISH! IT'S TOO LATE ALREADY.

DINNER THAT NIGHT WAS A BIT TOO QUIET.

FROM MY PARENTS' STRAY WORDS I CAME TO KNOW THE NEWS ABOUT OUR HOMELAND.

WE TRIED TO CONCENTRATE ON OUR QUOTA OF NAAN AND KEEMA AND FISH..

BUT QUOTAS VARY...

KEEMA AND NAAN FOR ME TOOOOO!!

HOW COME YOUR COLLEAGUES CAME SO LATE?

HUH?

WHERE ARE YOU GOING TO MEET TOMORROW?

AHH... WELL... AT RAHIM BHAI'S... AN OLD FRIEND.....

OTHERWISE, LIFE WENT ON IN OUR KARACHI LIKE A WEIGHTLESS FLIGHT

PALACE HOTEL

MY BROTHER PERVEZ CYCLED OFF TO SCHOOL

I HEADED TO THE UNIVERSITY.

BUS STOP

AND OUR LITTLE SISTER REMAINED SCHOOLWARD BOUND EVERYDAY.....

91

THE SITUATION CALLED FOR A SUBTLE SHIFT IN PERCEPTION. BY DAY, KARACHI SEEMED AS USUAL...

SUNNY AND SLIGHTLY CHILLY, SINCE IT WAS ALMOST NOVEMBER.

THE NIGHTS, HOWEVER, WERE SLOWLY CHANGING. SUNDOWN BROUGHT WITH IT FATHER'S SURREPTITIOUS TRIPS TO SECRET MEETINGS...

HE TOLD ME ALL ABOUT THEM, LATER. MUCH LATER.

TODAY'S MEETING IS SPECIAL...

DON'T KNOW WHAT TO SAY. TAKE CARE.

AND THE CROWD WAS GETTING BIGGER BY THE DAY, AT THIS SOMEPLACE ELSE.....

ALL I KNEW THEN WAS, THE NIGHTS WERE MEANT FOR SOMEPLACE ELSE...

AS-SALAAM ALAIKUM... RAHIM BHAI...

SALAAM ALAIKUM, DEAR AHMED BHAI ! SO, WHAT'S THE PLAN?

WORDS FLEW IN MANY DIRECTIONS.

THAT MEANS 6. LOOK, NUMERICAL PRIORITY IS NOT A QUESTION HERE . JUST TELL ME HOW READY YOU ARE TO TAKE RISKS.

PRECISELY, THAT'S WHY WE ARE HERE . WHAT SHOULD BE THE PLAN?

LOOK RAHIM BHAI, FOR EXAMPLE, MINE IS A FOUR-MEMBER FAMILY, PLUS PARENTS...

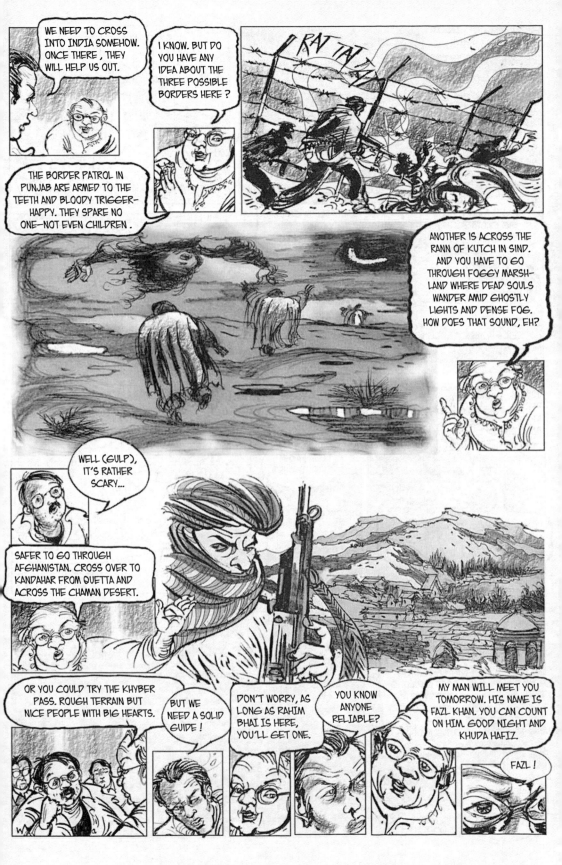

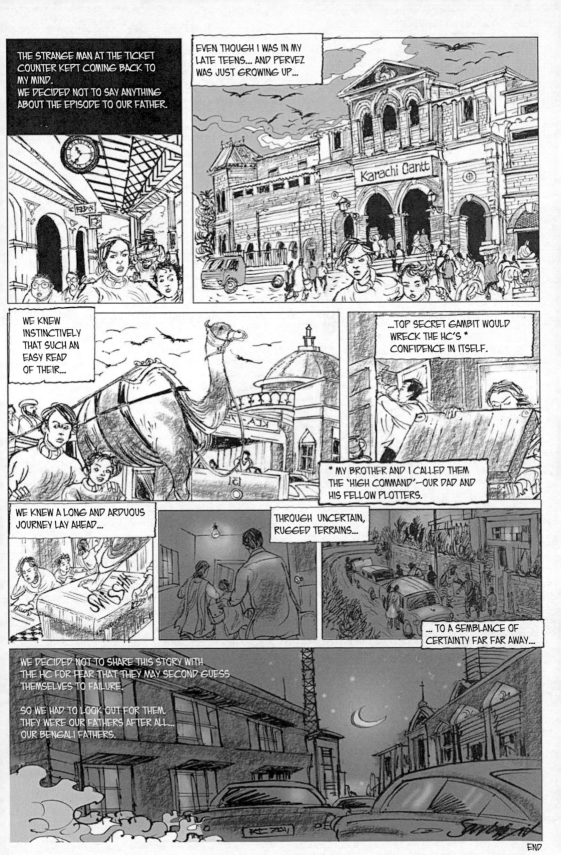

NINA SABNANI

is a filmmaker with expertise in animation and illustration.
She has been exploring the relationship between word and image
and bringing together animation and visual ethnography.
She is passionate about storytelling and working in collaboration
with traditional artists.

Her film *Tanko Bole Chhe (The Stitches Speak)* has won several
national and international awards. She has written and illustrated
several books for children for publishers like Tulika, Pratham and
Bookworm Goa.

Currently, she is Associate Professor at the Industrial Design Centre,
IIT Bombay.

KNOW
DIRECTIONS
HOME?

We travelled through the night and reached the border at daybreak.

The military stopped us. They would not let us pass.

There we were with all that we owned, our goats, our camels and so many kids.

YOU CANNOT COME INTO INDIA

But this is India now!

We sat down and refused to move.

They agreed on the condition that we get into the trucks. In good faith we did.

Three people stayed behind with the animals.
Over 100 people were packed into three trucks.

GET INTO THE TRUCK!

After rounds of rigorous counting, the convoy moved.
Soon, the morning arrived, with police jeeps leading the trucks.

After several hours my husband realised that we were heading back to the border and not India. He asked the driver.

Devoid of any expression, the driver said he was only following the other trucks. He did not know.

Stop! Stop!

In desperation, my husband asked the driver to stop so that we could stretch our legs and also relieve ourselves.

As we waited, the other trucks also returned.
The police tried hard but we just sat there.
Seven days went by, but we just sat there.

Several people of consequence tried convincing us to
retreat but we did not. And by now, more and more
people had begun to come in from the border.
A month had passed, but we just sat there.

GET INTO
THE
TRUCK!

No we won't. You are lying about
taking us to India. We will not get
into the trucks now. We will stay here
and die.

Soon, a politician came. He was called Daulat Bhai, and he tried to convince us that we were being taken to India. But he understood that we had lost trust. Then he gave us his promise and said we would be taken to Kutch initially, and later to Deesa.

We agreed for Kutch. With no other option, we got back into the trucks and they took off in another direction.

We will come for you within a week !

Like before, we had no idea where we were going.

It was late in the evening when we reached a hilly terrain,

where there was nothing.

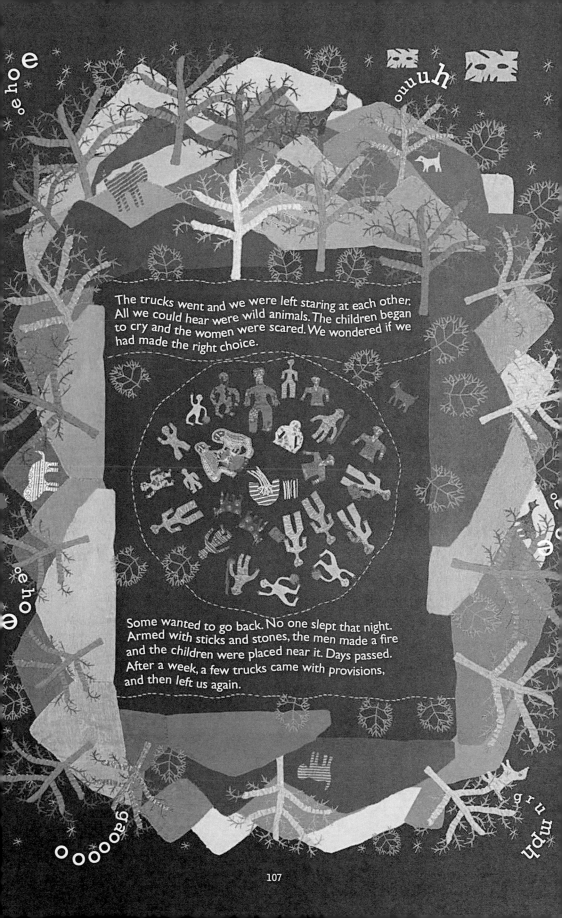

The trucks went and we were left staring at each other. All we could hear were wild animals. The children began to cry and the women were scared. We wondered if we had made the right choice.

Some wanted to go back. No one slept that night. Armed with sticks and stones, the men made a fire and the children were placed near it. Days passed. After a week, a few trucks came with provisions, and then left us again.

We realised that we were probably going to be there for a while, so we began to settle down slowly. Some people built Bhunga houses and chopped wood from trees.

The school teacher in my husband worried for our children, as they were just being idle.

He started teaching in a small Bhunga hut that slowly turned into a school, where most of our kids received their education. This soon drew a lot of interest.

Since we were a refugee camp, many people came to see us: politicians, social workers, government officials. Impressed with my husband's teaching skills, they made him the Headmaster and officially recognised the school.
My headmaster husband now had a small salary of Rs 300!

OK children, let's get together here

Eight years passed in the camp, and then the government changed. Soon, we were again visited by politicians and this time they were quite interested in our situation as refugees. We told them we had no identity in the country except as refugees.

OK! We declare you Indian citizens from today.

Was it that easy for them, I wondered. Who cared?
After eight long years the wait was finally over.
We now stood on a piece of land that was neither
Adigaam nor Deesa.

They gave us land with no water nearby.
With no water, farming life wasn't getting any easier.

We sold it and moved to Sumrasar where we felt we could
live and support ourselves.

I had learnt to do
Suf embroidery from
my grandmother
and found it useful.

Today we are a collective and we use our art not only to support ourselves but also to tell our stories.

When I look back I realise that my story is just one such instance; there are many others, untold.

Raniben Ratilal Bhanani,
Kala Raksha, Parkar Vas,
Sumrasar Sheikh,
Bhuj Taluka,
Gujarat.

End

ARIF AYAZ PARREY

is a Kashmiri writer and independent researcher.

He currently lives between Islamabad and Anantnag, Jammu & Kashmir.

WASIM HELAL

is a visual artist whose work revolves around the art of storytelling,
designing books, writing and illustrating graphic stories, and collaborating
with documentary and other filmmakers.

His first project was illustrating and designing a bilingual children's book,
Cuentos de Espana, by Spanish writer AR Almodovar. He has designed book covers
for leading publishing houses in India.
In 2011 three of his short graphic sequentials were exhibited at Bricklane Gallery,
London. In 2012, his graphic novella *Monochrome* was published in the
Lalit Kala Akademi art journal.

He lives and works in Kolkata.

TAMASHA-e-
TETWAL

Ah the slippery smell of sotsal!

114

116

117

Hope the ride was not too bumpy, son.

Not at all, janab!

That is nice to hear. So, jigra, what do you want to know about the story?

118

I proceed to give him a lengthy explanation.

When i'm finished, his gaze lingers on my face, as if probing for the last specks of meaning.

विश्व के शक्तिशाली देशों में जगह बना रहा है हमارے دین میں بات کی کوئی جگہ نہیں

I have been around for a long time, son.

The world has become an insufferable place. There is too much noise. Take this story for example.

How easy it has turned out to be for the rulers to cloak it with the racket of Partition.

The death of a Kashmiri dog has been justified as a tragedy of an imaginary partition, not a real one.

And how slickly the dog has been made both an Indian and a Pakistani when he is neither.

What does that mean?

It means there was no India in this territorial sense before the British.

The British forged it by force and deceit.

119

While returning I sit beside the angry river.

As the conductor said, the bus is not going to leave for another half an hour.

My mother once told me...

Never go too close to a loud river...

Its sound will mesmerise and pull you in.

Suddenly...

True, the razzle-dazzle of the big cities is seducing these children.

What is it?

Mushrooms.

They are much greener and bigger there.

Do you like them?

As a matter of fact...

I do.

Then you should stay for the night and have some with dinner.

The bus is about to leave, hurry up!

Not today, thanks.

But there is always a next time.

End

From and for
Parvaiz Bukhari and Ajjaz Hussain.

127

ARUNDHATI GHOSH

writes poetry in Bangla and works for an arts foundation.
She loves journeys and maps.

Arundhati lives and works in Bangalore.

APPUPEN

is a comics creator and artist who tells stories from the original mythical
world, Halahala.

His first graphic novel, *Moonward* (Blaft, 2009) was selected for the
Angouleme International Comics Festival in France, 2011. His second graphic
novel, *Legends of Halahala* (HarperCollins India, 2013) has been called India's
first silent graphic novel. Appupen is currently working on his next graphic novel,
'Aspyrus'.

Appupen's original art has been exhibited in galleries in Bangalore, Chennai
and Kochi. His commissioned murals and art can also be seen in many cities
across India and at www.georgemathen.com.

He currently lives in Bangalore.

{Photo courtesy: Amyth Venkatramaiah}

WATER STORIES

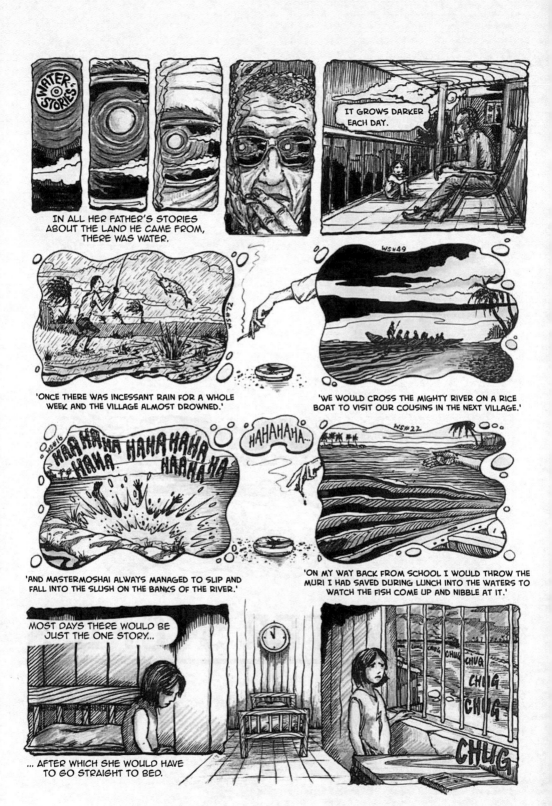

WATER STORIES

IT GROWS DARKER EACH DAY.

IN ALL HER FATHER'S STORIES ABOUT THE LAND HE CAME FROM, THERE WAS WATER.

'ONCE THERE WAS INCESSANT RAIN FOR A WHOLE WEEK AND THE VILLAGE ALMOST DROWNED.'

'WE WOULD CROSS THE MIGHTY RIVER ON A RICE BOAT TO VISIT OUR COUSINS IN THE NEXT VILLAGE.'

'AND MASTERMOSHAI ALWAYS MANAGED TO SLIP AND FALL INTO THE SLUSH ON THE BANKS OF THE RIVER.'

'ON MY WAY BACK FROM SCHOOL I WOULD THROW THE MURI I HAD SAVED DURING LUNCH INTO THE WATERS TO WATCH THE FISH COME UP AND NIBBLE AT IT.'

MOST DAYS THERE WOULD BE JUST THE ONE STORY...

... AFTER WHICH SHE WOULD HAVE TO GO STRAIGHT TO BED.

130

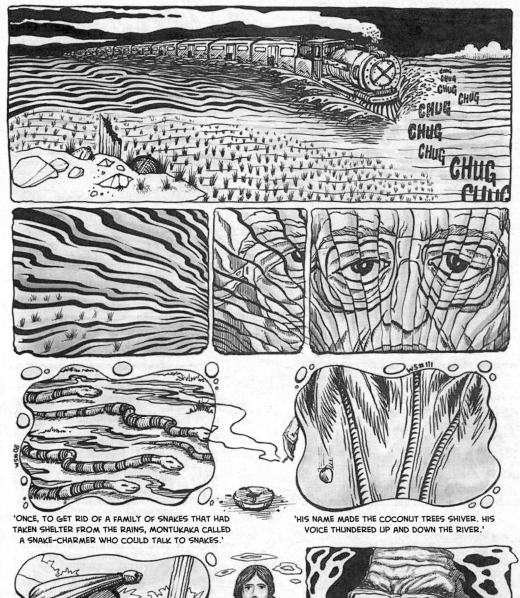

'ONCE, TO GET RID OF A FAMILY OF SNAKES THAT HAD TAKEN SHELTER FROM THE RAINS, MONTUKAKA CALLED A SNAKE-CHARMER WHO COULD TALK TO SNAKES.'

'HIS NAME MADE THE COCONUT TREES SHIVER. HIS VOICE THUNDERED UP AND DOWN THE RIVER.'

'HE WAS A NOTORIOUS RIVER PIRATE, OUR ANCESTOR, THE RIVER ROBIN HOOD.'

HIS EYES WOULD SHINE WITH PRIDE.

131

'MY MOTHER AND AUNTS WORSHIPPED THE RIVER. MY AUNT WHO HAD NO CHILDREN, ADOPTED THE RIVER AS HER DAUGHTER AND DROWNED RED SARIS IN IT.'

'THE LOCAL MENDICANT SPOKE CHANTS INTO A BOWL OF WATER THAT CAST AWAY DEMONS WHO FREQUENTED THE BODIES OF YOUNG GIRLS.'

'I WOULD OFTEN STEAL THE BOWL OF WATER AND DRINK IT UP QUICKLY.'

BUT WHEN HE SPOKE OF THE PADMA HE SEEMED DISTURBED.

THE RIVER HAD MADE AND RUINED MANY LIVES.

THE STORIES OF THE PADMA WOULD ALWAYS BREAK MIDWAY, HALT AT THE EDGE, PAUSE, UNFINISHED...

HER MOTHER HAD BEEN ILL FOR A WHILE AND DIED IN HER SLEEP AT THE HOSPITAL.

ICU

MY MOTHER DID NOT DIE OF ANY ILLNESS, YOU KNOW.

WHAT?

'THE PADMA SWALLOWED HER.'

'IT ATE HER UP. MY BEAUTIFUL MOTHER. SHE WENT INTO THE RIVER ONE AFTERNOON AND NEVER CAME BACK.'

'I THINK THE PADMA KNEW WE WERE LEAVING FOR ANOTHER LAND. SHE STOLE MY MOTHER.'

132

BABA!

NO, NO. IT WAS A CURSE OF THE PADMA.

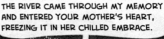

COME ON BABA. MA WAS ILL FOR SOME TIME.

THE RIVER CAME THROUGH MY MEMORY AND ENTERED YOUR MOTHER'S HEART, FREEZING IT IN HER CHILLED EMBRACE.

WHAT ARE YOU SAYING? YOU ALWAYS SAID...

MAYBE SHE CURSED YOUR MOTHER TOO. MAYBE IT'S BECAUSE OF ME. SOMEHOW ALL THE PEOPLE I LOVE....

THE RIVER HAS NOTHING TO DO WITH IT.

'BECAUSE OF ME, I AM THE ONE CURSED BY HER – RAKSHASI PADMA – WILL YOU NEVER FORGIVE ME FOR MY EXILE?'

SOMETIMES, AFTER HE HAD MOVED ACROSS THE NEW BORDER, THE 'NISHIDAAK' WOULD CALL HIM AT NIGHT TO THE RIVER.

'I HAD AN AMULET THEN, WASHED IN ENCHANTED WATER.'

'HOW WILL I PROTECT YOU? ARE THERE OTHERS IN YOUR CITY? WILL THEY BURN YOUR HOUSE, SCREAMING THE NAMES OF THEIR GODS?'

HE KEPT GOING BACK TO THE PAST AND RETURNING TO THE PRESENT, MIXING UP HER MOTHER WITH HIS MOTHER,

FORGIVE ME, FORGIVE ME.

THE RIVER WITH THE RELENTLESS KOLKATA RAIN AND HIS EXILE SO MANY YEARS AGO TO HER MOTHER'S DEATH TODAY.

SHE DID NOT SLEEP THAT NIGHT. HIS RANTS WERE BEGINNING TO AFFECT HER.

SHE TOUCHED THE BARRENNESS INSIDE HER.

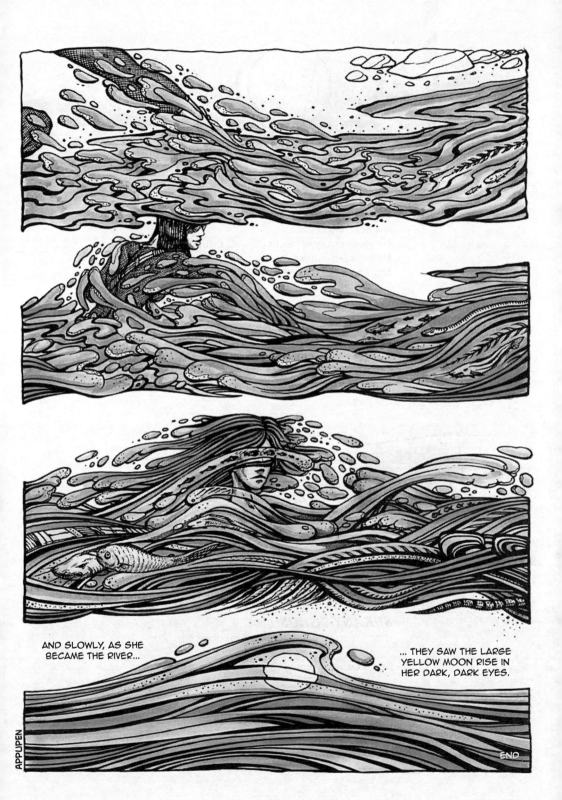

AND SLOWLY, AS SHE BECAME THE RIVER...

... THEY SAW THE LARGE YELLOW MOON RISE IN HER DARK, DARK EYES.

APPUPEN

END

M HASAN
is a poet and activist.
He occasionally writes in Bengali Little Magazines.
He has been editing literary magazines like *Daw*
and *Kadamati*, published in Dhaka.

His first book of poetry, *Dinlipi,* was published in 2011.
He has also co-edited the collected works of Monjatuddin
and Tauhid Enam.

He lives with his little family in Muelheim an der Ruhr, Germany.

SUKANYA GHOSH
is an artist, animator and general dogsbody.

She is currently based between Delhi and Calcutta.

MAKING OF A
POET

15 April 2009, Dhaka.

It was *Nababarsha*, the Bengali New Year.
While the entire city prepared for the festivities,
I was on my way to Jalpaiguri.

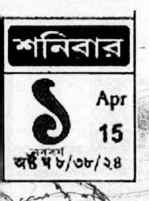

An overnight bus journey to the Northern Changrabandha-Burimari border,
crossing the Teesta twice. The legendary Teesta, over which governments fight,
elections are won, looked splendid that New Year morning.

From the beginning, I was both curious and nervous about the journey. I was to
meet him—the poet—for the first time. That's where I was headed, across the
border, to the other Bengal.

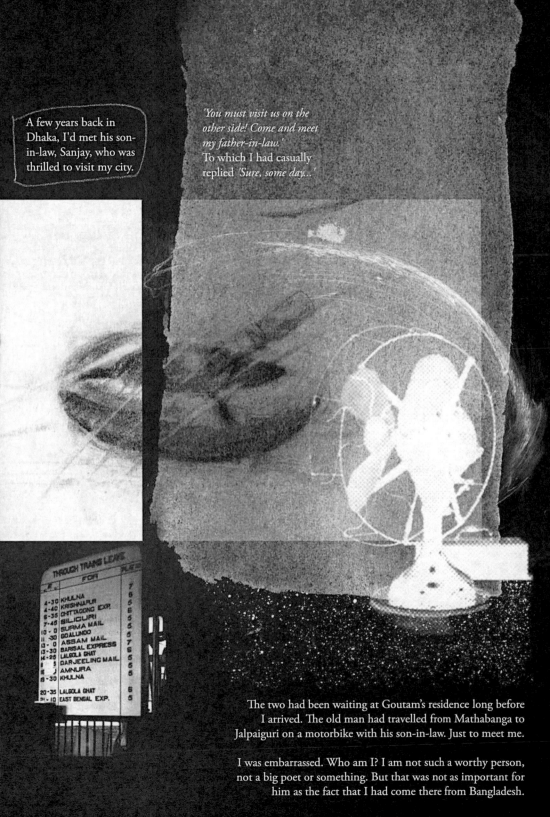

A few years back in Dhaka, I'd met his son-in-law, Sanjay, who was thrilled to visit my city.

'You must visit us on the other side! Come and meet my father-in-law.'
To which I had casually replied *'Sure, some day...'*

The two had been waiting at Goutam's residence long before I arrived. The old man had travelled from Mathabanga to Jalpaiguri on a motorbike with his son-in-law. Just to meet me.

I was embarrassed. Who am I? I am not such a worthy person, not a big poet or something. But that was not as important for him as the fact that I had come there from Bangladesh.

And as I looked at him talking to me with his smiling face, I could smell it in him. The Bangladesh inside him flowing like a small river, a very personal one, much cherished and well taken care of.

1957
He had travelled to India from Bangladesh as a small boy with his father, and life was never easy thereafter. Then, with some education and a job, he started writing; the things he had to do to survive made a poet out of him.

'With father's death, all seemed lost. No money, no energy. It was impossible to survive. But then, moving to Kuchbihar was a wise decision. Over there I met some good people, they helped me out. And once I had a stable job, I began writing again.'

Damn!
This was all but a poet's story.
I was getting nervous now.

He talked of Sirajganj, Bajar Vodroghat, his birthplace and the place of his childhood, again and again, of the people there were once, of the places, of the big banyan tree, of the river ghat, of Penu da and all.

141

I asked him, What does it mean, the land to a poet? He answered, 'The birds, the trees, don't belong to some particular land. There is a real land that exists outside and there is one in the imagination.'

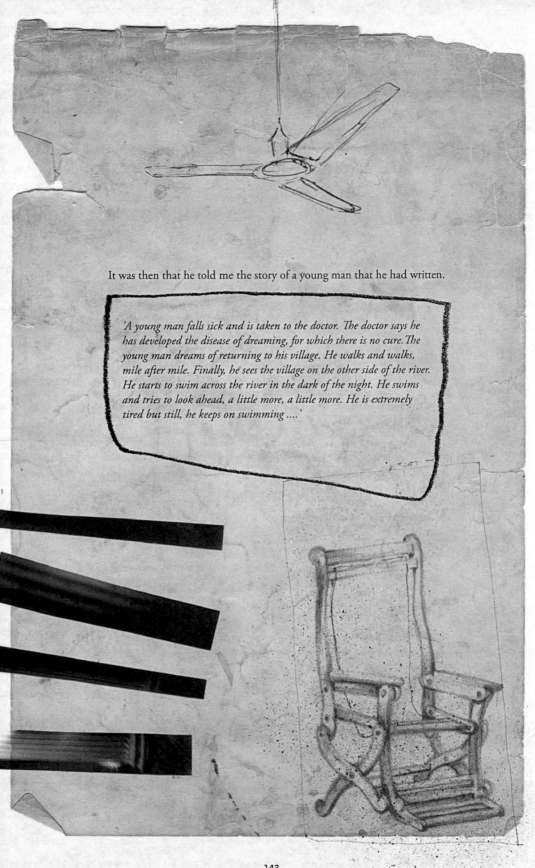

It was then that he told me the story of a young man that he had written.

'A young man falls sick and is taken to the doctor. The doctor says he has developed the disease of dreaming, for which there is no cure. The young man dreams of returning to his village. He walks and walks, mile after mile. Finally, he sees the village on the other side of the river. He starts to swim across the river in the dark of the night. He swims and tries to look ahead, a little more, a little more. He is extremely tired but still, he keeps on swimming ....'

143

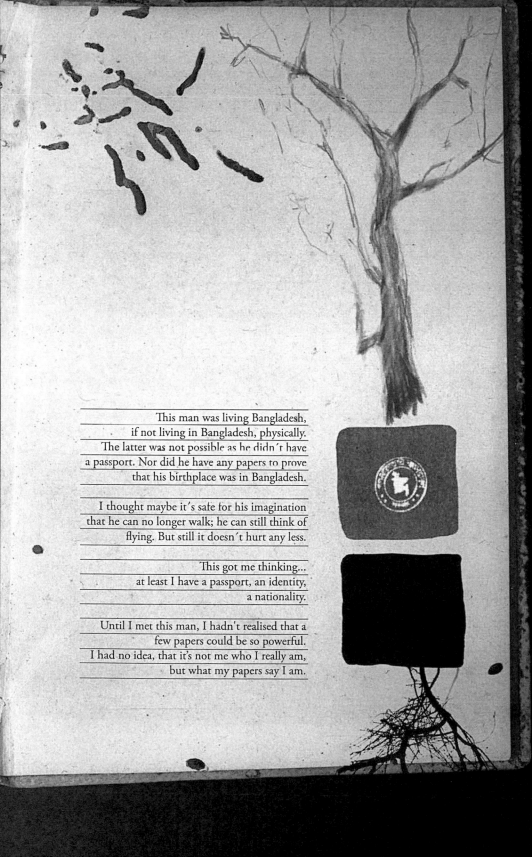

This man was living Bangladesh,
if not living in Bangladesh, physically.
The latter was not possible as he didn´t have
a passport. Nor did he have any papers to prove
that his birthplace was in Bangladesh.

I thought maybe it´s safe for his imagination
that he can no longer walk; he can still think of
flying. But still it doesn´t hurt any less.

This got me thinking...
at least I have a passport, an identity,
a nationality.

Until I met this man, I hadn't realised that a
few papers could be so powerful.
I had no idea, that it's not me who I really am,
but what my papers say I am.

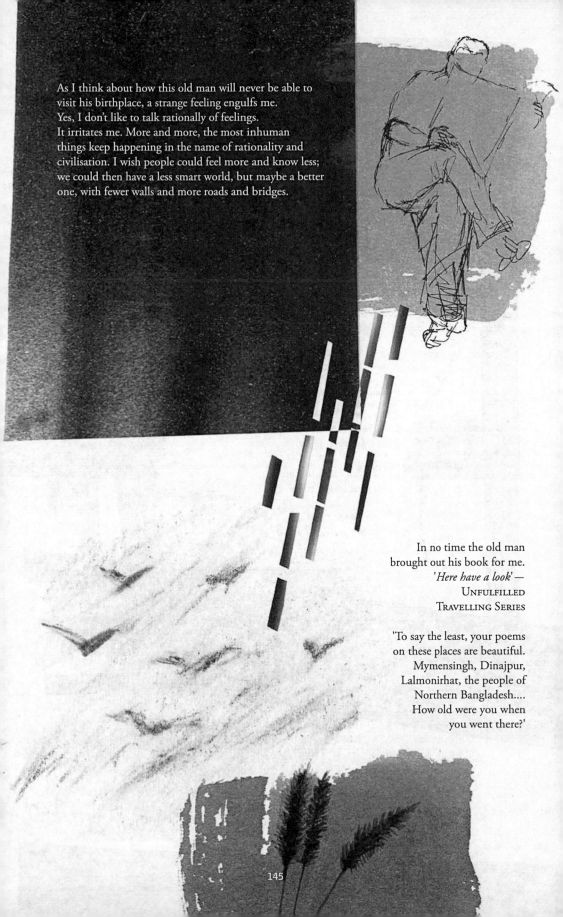

As I think about how this old man will never be able to
visit his birthplace, a strange feeling engulfs me.
Yes, I don't like to talk rationally of feelings.
It irritates me. More and more, the most inhuman
things keep happening in the name of rationality and
civilisation. I wish people could feel more and know less;
we could then have a less smart world, but maybe a better
one, with fewer walls and more roads and bridges.

In no time the old man
brought out his book for me.
'Here have a look' —
UNFULFILLED
TRAVELLING SERIES

'To say the least, your poems
on these places are beautiful.
Mymensingh, Dinajpur,
Lalmonirhat, the people of
Northern Bangladesh....
How old were you when
you went there?'

For the poet, the one I got to know,
Nitya Malakar.

147   end

VISHWAJYOTI GHOSH

is the author of the graphic novel *Delhi Calm* (HarperCollins India, 2010). His comics are regularly published in various journals and anthologies, including *When Kulbhushan Met Stockli, Ctrl.Alt.Shift Unmasks Corruption* and *Pao Anthology of Comics*. He is also a member of the Pao Comics Collective.

In 2009 he published a collection of postcards based on classified ads titled *Times New Roman & Countrymen*. Vishwajyoti Ghosh is also the author of the cartoon column *FULL TOSS*. Associated with Inverted Commas, a communication collective, he is currently wrapping up a mapping project in the working clusters of Gurgaon.

He lives and works in New Delhi.

AMIYA SEN (1916–90)

is a Bengali novelist and short story writer whose writings have been published in various Bengali journals, including *Desh, Jugantar,* and *Basumati*. She engaged with the world of migrants and refugees through most of her writings.

Apart from her non-fiction books, *Aranyalipi* and *New Delhi-r Nepathye,* she also wrote *Shonai Shono Rupkatha,* a children's book and a memoir of her childhood engagement with the Indian freedom movement.

A GOOD EDUCATION

{Acknowledgement: SARAI-CSDS Independent Fellowship}

Texts by Amiya Sen are from *Aranyalipi* (The Forest Chronicles), based
on her interactions and experiences in the refugee camps of Dandakaranya.
Translated from Bengali by Bhaswati Ghosh

Bye Babu. Be good and don't be naughty. See you in the evening.

1975, it must have been. The moment my mother left for work, I was the Prince of 7, Kasturba Niketan, a rehabilitation home for partition refugees, tucked in a corner of Lajpat Nagar, New Delhi. My government servant-grandmother, blessed with staff quarters here, took care of the roof above. For me, the day was blissful in the company of Dadu, my retired grandfather and Didu—my in-and-out grandmother—who would return in time to feed her grandson.

Where from?

Reba Mandal from Khulna

Now hurry up will you?

AMIYA SEN

Assistant Superintendent cum Matron, Kasturba Niketan

150

Dear One,
Welcome to the Dandakaranya Project.
The Raipur station isn't far from these
desolate plains. This place feels peaceful
but on its edge. I am told right now 35,000 are
living here in Mana Camp. Farmers, sweet-makers,
blacksmiths, potters and cobblers from East Bengal.
Unlike us, the privileged who moved at the very outset,
these are the real lambs of partition. Pushed by the
unanticipated attack of death, they reached the Indian border.
The very sight of them made the West Bengal government
scream, 'There's no space here — we can't accommodate them.'
Despite being unlettered and helpless, they show such dignity!
But who will understand! We are such a self-oblivious race.

152

I am here on work. Simply put, here my job is to counsel and convince mothers to send their kids to Delhi. The government promises these children a good education in Kasturba Niketan. I never felt the scheme was bad yet my fear was, would they agree? They would have to let go of their children for years! That's exactly how it was meant to work. These boys and girls wouldn't be returning before they could be on their own. We are talking of 15–20 years. Here, their world changes within minutes; who knows if Mana Camp will exist when they return? Even if it does, these destitute women might get lost in the deep crannies of the forest.

In *Apple Cart*, Bernard Shaw described the working of a democratic government: as fire engulfed a house, the fire brigade was called. Before the firefighters arrived, not only did the house turn into ashes, but a new building had replaced the old one. But how could the firemen leave without fulfilling their obligations? Before leaving, they ensured the new building was drenched. Brick by brick.

Dear one, couldn't something better have been planned for them? Couldn't there be a home similar to the one in Delhi somewhere in West Bengal — a familiar land?

Anyway, the project's focus was education. For this reason, it wasn't feasible to take the entire family to Delhi. I hadn't revealed to them that along with their children, they were going to lose their dole money too.
Still, I fought on with my dilemmas — remember I was here on work.

154

KASTURBA NIKETAN
(UNDER MINISTRY OF REHABILITATION SERVICES)

WIDOW HOSTEL

MENTAL ASYLUM

We are not Refugees. We have our Yellow Cards. We are 'PL', 'Permanent Liability'.

How are you finding Delhi? Whatever it is, Alomati, make sure your daughter goes to school.

Don't ask, Didi. Now she wants to get married to that Punjabi driver...

I took a different route and started describing the facilities of Kasturba Niketan in great detail—electricity, water, fan, clean beds, nice, big rooms, great education. Then I used my ultimate weapon—an appeal to mother's love.

You love your children so much; let them live because of that love. Let them be established in society. Kids who show interest will be sent up to college. Just imagine how big your children will be! Here, is it any good that they grow up hungry, at someone else's mercy? In Delhi, everything will be free!

With 165 Punjabi and 125 Bengali families, most of the Bengali lot at Mana Camp were transferred to Kasturba Niketan in 1967. Kasturba Niketan had three adjacent buildings—an administrative building, a hostel for Bengali widows and their children, and a mental asylum. Often the asylum inmates would sneak into the widows' hostel creating havoc for the caretakers.

For Didu, being a Bengali did not make life any bit easier. For the widows she was 'adminstration', hence responsible for the life they lived. And since they both spoke the same language, she would often receive a generous dose of their curses. On a good day, she was just one of them.

As for me—the grandson of 'adminstration', I enjoyed getting pampered from all sides.

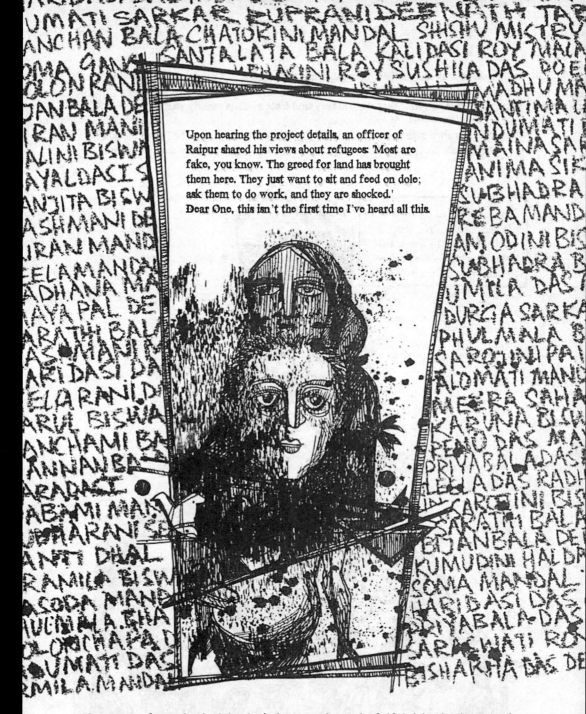

Upon hearing the project details, an officer of Raipur shared his views about refugees: 'Most are fake, you know. The greed for land has brought them here. They just want to sit and feed on dole; ask them to do work, and they are shocked.' Dear One, this isn't the first time I've heard all this.

No one came forward to heal the physical or mental wounds of this helpless lot that not only suffered violence, lost their loved ones, but were also rendered homeless and insecure. Instead, they were packed like sardines inside train coaches. Before they could gather their bearings they found themselves in unfamiliar territory. The riverine lot were now landlocked burdens on the state. But, Dear One, who made it so difficult? On the other side, Pakistan's policy shows no confusion. Its policies with regard to minorities in East Bengal are no different from its attitude towards Pakhtuns and the other minorities of NWFP. Therefore, heaping blame on Pakistan is futile.

In the end, most of the mothers relented. When they agreed, my heart ached with a void. Where will these children return after 15 years? Will they have even a faint memory of Mana Camp then? Even if they do, will they find their mothers eagerly waiting for them?

Dear One, you are a man and might laugh at this. But I am a mother and all these thoughts crossed my mind. Seeing some of them agree, I shivered. I had played the devil's advocate.

Take them with you.
We don't wish to see them.
Let them stand on their
own feet;
that's all we want.

You'll be surprised to hear that this latter
category of women happened to be the
majority. These women crossed the sea of
death to come so far and were at the very end
of their tether. They were willing to let go
of their only support—their children. I stood
frozen. Delhi would be happy, for them
I had succeeded.

Mana Camp, March 1965.

Suited-booted, enjoying the privilege of
being held by the refugee kids.
Kasturba Niketan, Lajpat Nagar, New Delhi.

Fade to white....

BANI ABIDI

is an artist who uses video and photography to comment on politics
and culture, often through humorous and absurd vignettes.
Abidi received a BFA from the National College of Arts, Lahore
in 1995 and an MFA from the School of the Art Institute of Chicago
in 2000. Her work has been exhibited widely in solo and group shows
internationally. They include Documenta 13, Germany (2012);
Bani Abidi—Section Yellow, Baltic Centre for Contemporary Art, UK (2011);
The Global Contemporary. Art Worlds After 1989, ZKM | Center for Art and Media,
Karlsruhe; *Where Three Dreams Cross,* Whitechapel Art Gallery, London (2010);
Xth Lyon Biennale, Lyon, France (2009); 7th Gwangju Biennale 2008, Kwangju,
South Korea; *Thermocline of Art—New Asian Waves, ZKM,* Karlsruhe,Germany (2007);
Singapore Biennale, Singapore (2006); Sub-Contingent—*The South Asian Sub Continent*
in Contemporary Art, Fondazione Sandretto Re Rebaudengo, Turin, Italy (2006);
Contemporary Commonwealth, National Gallery of Victoria, Australia (2006);
3rd Fukuoka Asian Art Triennale, Fukuoka, Japan (2005).
Her work is in the collections of the MoMANY, Guggenheim NY, Tate Modern,
The British Museum, The Fukuoka Asian Art Museum and the Devi Art Foundation,
among others.

She is now working in Berlin.

Confrontation between Pakistani and Indian Confrontation between Indian and Pakistani

THE NEWS

{Adapted from the original video produced at
Khoj International Artists Residency, 2001}

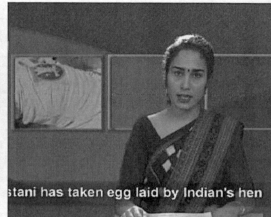

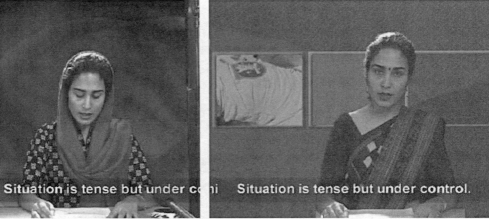

ANKUR AHUJA
is a cinematographer, photographer, editor
and intermittent food blogger.

She is based in Delhi and is currently working
on her first Bollywood feature.

THE RED LEDGER

{Translated from Hindi by the author}

My grandfather was unusually attached to his red ledgers.
He used to order them in bulk from the best in the business.

Delivery for you sir.

Thanks!

Bound
in red cloth,
stitched with
white thread,
it was his
daily diary
of profit and loss.

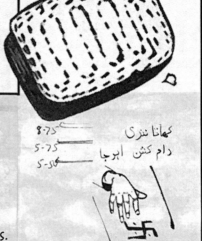

Every night, after dinner, he would sit hunched over the red book, fingers stained with ink, furiously calculating, recording, keeping a meticulous account of debits and credits. In Urdu, a language that no one else in the family could read.

...Then he flew to the moon!

accounts

To me it was his personal diary filled with stories of adventure lurking under his stoic character.

When he walked into Delhi, bewildered and dispossessed, he was allocated a house on the margins of a very cosmopolitan and desirable address. He moved in with his wife and two kids and his brother's family of five.

At that time, just down the road from him, Nirad C Chaudhuri was busy penning his 'The Autobiography of an Unknown Indian.'

I used to live on Nicholson Road and your grandfather was in Mori Gate...

The one-room house was partitioned to create an illusion of space.

My grandmother's jewellery helped set up a new life—that and the sewing machine which came as compensation.

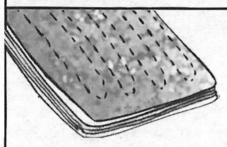

Bada Bazaar

Bahawalpur, Pakistan.

Sometimes he spoke about what was and what could have been.

The massive shops he had left behind, his friends, the exemplary brotherhood of Hindus and Muslims...

...Moon Sahab, a British official from Bahawalpur who promised to send his three suitcases to the new address in India...

...and that last evening in Bada Bazaar, Bahawalpur...

You're Dead!

The story of his life always ended there. I didn't have the courage to ask further; maybe I just didn't want to see him cry.

Many years after his death my grandmother filled the gaps. She told me she was actually his second wife. His first wife had died soon after his marriage. For years after, he would spend hours sitting in the park, crying.

Brought up by a blind uncle, he lost his parents to an epidemic in his early childhood. One of his sisters was abducted during the journey from Bahawalpur to Delhi. She found her way back much later but my grandmother refused to discuss what had happened with her.

A lot of those stories died with my grandfather, and the rest wandered around in those red ledgers filled with grandiose black squiggles in Urdu, that none of us ever learnt to read.

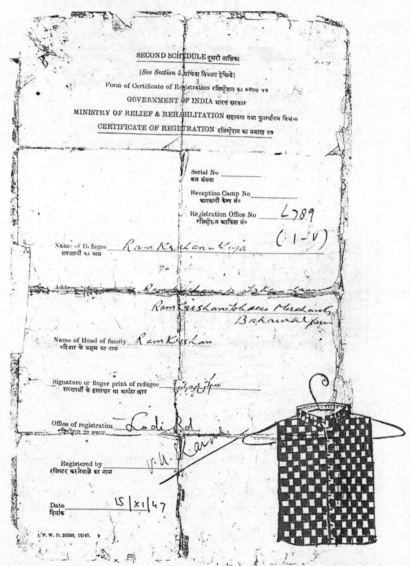

After he died, all his red ledgers were sold to the kabadi. All that remains of him is a certificate from the Ministry of Relief and Rehabilitation that confirmed his status—a refugee.

End

AHMAD RAFAY ALAM
is a lawyer, environmental activist and avid cyclist.
He lives in Lahore with his wife and daughter.
You can follow him on Twitter @rafay_alam

MARTAND KHOSLA
is an architect and artist. He is a founding partner of RKDS,
a design studio established in 2001.
His artwork engages with ideas of labour, urbanisation and displacement.

He lives in New Delhi.

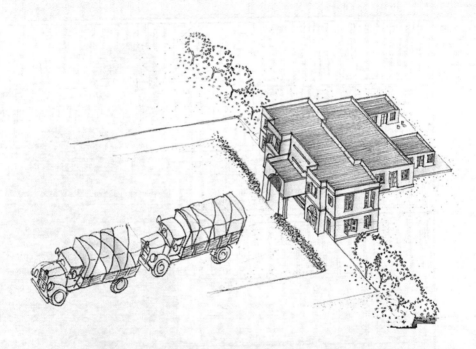

90 UPPER MALL
or 1 Bawa Park

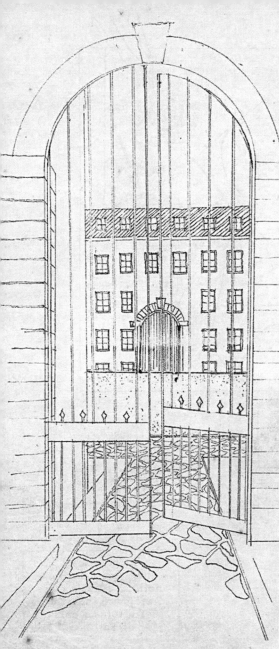

I was born into one of those families that presume one will complete one's studies at a Western university. And so, like many other Pakistani students who read law in the United Kingdom, I was preparing for my bar qualification as a student barrister at Lincoln's Inn, though the bar was dreadfully boring and, as I later discovered back home, also irrelevant to the Pakistani legal system. At the time, however, I felt lucky to have found accommodation in William Goodenough House or 'Willie G' in London's quiet Mecklenburgh Square.

Willie G had quite a few Pakistani residents. I once heard an admissions tutor comment about how it was dangerous to recruit more than a dozen Pakistanis into any academic programme: 'They form a cricket team and never do any work'—a good idea and an almost true observation.

It was in Willie G that I became friends
with Martand Khosla, a student of architecture
from India. We hit it off immediately.
For a Pakistani like me this was a great way to
know about the country next door that figured
so prominently in defining what my country was.
I had no notion of what India was other than the
opinions I'd picked up from school textbooks,
television and the press. You get the picture?

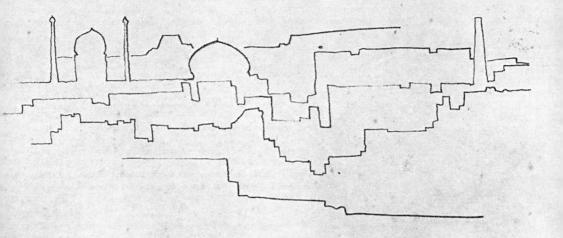

As it inevitably happens in this part of the world, we discovered some
social connections. Besides many recent ones, I learnt that both
his grandparents and my father shared the same alma mater,
Lahore's famous Government College. I learnt that part of
Martand's family was from Lahore and had left for India during
Partition. I've always been a proud Lahori, a vekhiya nahin tay jamiya nahin
(if you ain't seen it, you ain't seen nothin') sort, and his connections
with the city of my birth, along with his wit and intelligence, made my
relationship with Martand stronger. One evening Martand barged into
my room at Willie G and said, in mock outrage...

When she left Lahore to spend the summer of 1947 in Simla, Shakuntala Khosla had no idea she would never see the city of her birth again. The wife of a High Court judge, she had only just won the ladies' singles title at the grass courts of the Lahore Gymkhana.

The club had offered to loan her the trophy for a short period, but she declined. She was confident enough about her game to say that she would take it from the club permanently if she won again the following year.

Shakuntala was the daughter of Bawa Natha Singh, Chief Engineer of Canals, in the service of the British Raj. Bawa Natha Singh dug into his savings and bought himself some land outside Lahore, on the other side of the canal, near the railway track that marked the outer limits of the Lahore Cantonment. In the mid-1920s, he built a series of bungalows including 1 Bawa Park, a stately home surrounded by gardens. Eventually when the land fell under the control of the Lahore Improvement Trust, the house was given an official number—90 Upper Mall.

In 1928, Shakuntala was married to GD Khosla, a promising young
Additional District & Sessions judge, in her father's newly built house.
Although posted in various districts in the Punjab, Shakuntala
remembers bringing up her children in the sprawling gardens flowing
from the courtyard of 90 Upper Mall. Later, GD Khosla was elevated to
the Lahore High Court and the couple moved their family into their official
residence at 7 Club Road, GOR. In the summer of 1947, there was 'talk'
expecting violence at the Partition. But the Khosla family dismissed it as
nothing more than bazaar gossip. It was only as late as July that it became
clear that the threat was real and they needed to make a decision fast.
Judging by the way things were, GD Khosla and family opted for India.
As the families of the Lahore High Court judges did every year, Shakuntala
and the children were spending their vacations in Simla.
Because of the threat of violence, she never returned to Lahore to collect
her belongings. GD Khosla himself drove down to Lahore, rented a few
trucks and, with the assistance of his friend Manzur Qadir, collected all his
belongings from 7 Club Road, GOR. On his way out of the city, GD Khosla
stopped by 90 Upper Mall and collected some of his father-in-law's
belongings. That was the last time a member of the Bawa Natha Singh
family set eyes on 90 Upper Mall.

***

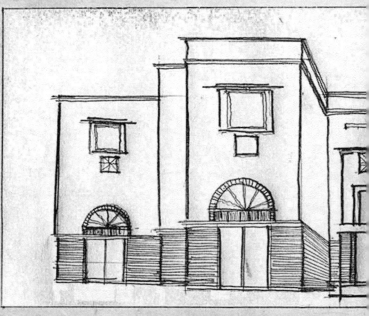

Mr and Mrs Mehmood Alam, my paternal grandparents,
shifted to Lahore some time around Partition.

Mehmood Alam had the distinction of being the only person to have
played Wimbledon as an Indian (in 1938, when he lost in a qualifying
round) and as a Pakistani (1948, when he did qualify but didn't get
much further than that).

I mention this because it was his dexterity with the racquet that
got him a job at Bird & Co., the largest trading house in India at the
time. During the build-up to Partition, the company decided to move
Mehmood Alam, their Delhi manager, to Lahore. Best to have a Muslim
manager for Muslim Pakistan's Lahore, they must have thought.
Prudent.

The move wasn't easy. After Partition, with the flood of mohajirs into
the newly formed Pakistan, arrived a flood of compensation claims.
Families that had opted to migrate to Pakistan were 'compensated' for
what they had left behind. They were often allocated the properties
that millions of Hindus and Sikhs had left behind when fleeing the
violence of Partition into the relative safety of India. As observed by a
New Yorker at the time, the Pakistani establishment was as mature as
a gang of enthusiastic novices; the compensation claims succumbed to
manipulation. The matter was politicised and, in no time, became the
source of great corruption.

Mr and Mrs Alam, parents of two children, with a third on the
way, were anxious to find a home to settle into. They too were
'compensated' with a house from the lot left to pick from.

***

Shakuntala with Martand's father, Romi

Mehmood Alam in his India jacket

90 Upper Mall. Located on Mall Road, between the canal and the Cantonment, it was a house some powerful bureaucrats had their eyes on. After years of living in a variety of flats, friends' homes and rented bungalows, the Alams found themselves a home in Pakistan.
According to the Record of Permanent Transfers kept by the Board of Evacuee Property, Mehmood Alam was transferred to 90 Upper Mall in November 1959.
My father, the eldest of Surrayya and Mehmood's children, was married in the front lawns of 90 Upper Mall. So was my sister and later, I. The house is huge, large enough to allow my grandparents and two successive generations to live comfortably.
I've lived in the back of 90 Upper Mall for the better part of my life. The house has been thoroughly lived in over the past half-century, and is now firmly associated with my family, the Alams of Upper Mall.

In April 2000, Romi Khosla, GD Khosla's youngest son was in London for work and came over to Willie G to visit his son, Martand. Over dinner, Martand told his father how he knew someone—me—in the building who was from Lahore. Romi had actually visited 90 Upper Mall a few years earlier while visiting Lahore.
He had been shown around the city of his birth and his grandfather's house by the poet Faiz's daughter, artist Salima Hashmi. He remembered meeting some people who lived there. Over dinner, as the Khoslas talked, the penny dropped. Yes! I bloody live in Martand's fu**ing house!

Hence, Martand barged into my room at Willie G and said what he said in mock outrage.

Martand and I tell this story every time we meet people together. We've gotten quite good at it. For us, the story is interesting because of the sheer coincidence of it all. Every time we tell it, we also rediscover the absurd and arbitrary nature of Partition. If it weren't for Partition, 90 Upper Mall would have remained a Khosla house, and I wouldn't have the identity that I have.

Having retold the story so many times, I now associate Partition with how my family came to live in Martand's house.

The rhetoric of Partition has always been characterised by loss and violence. Yet, in writing this or reflecting on the story, I can't but think of Partition in terms I'm familiar with: the story of 90 Upper Mall. Maybe this has been our buffer against the prejudices of history.

***

Rafay in conversation with Shakuntala Khosla. New Delhi, 2010.

End

SONYA FATAH

is a writer and editor from Karachi, Pakistan.
She discovered the complications of an Indo-Pak
identity by accident, when she and her husband moved
to India in 2006. Apart from writing and raising her children,
she runs a trust called No Man's Land, a platform
for South Asian engagement on ideas and action.

She lives and works out of New Delhi.

ARCHANA SREENIVASAN

illustrates for magazines, picture books, comics and lifestyle products.
She enjoys exploring new styles and techniques, and has illustrated
for periodicals like *Forbes Life* magazine and *The Mint* newspaper; publishers
such as Karadi Tales and Katha; and publications like *Manta Ray Comics,* Rusk
Bond's *The Blue Umbrella* and *Angry River.*
She likes cats, travelling, exploring the great outdoors, bird-watching,
and doodling in cafés.

She lives in Bengaluru.

KARACHI–DELHI
KATHA

KARACHI

♪ mmm   hmmmm... ♪

Aur, Sonya, how does it feel to live in India?

It looks really wonderful on TV....

Haan, Paro, India is good. Took me a while to adjust. Life's very similar and very different there. Not exactly like you see on TV.

We were also thinking of going. Hemu is after my life to go there. Says 'let's show it to the children'...but...

But... she never listens to me. After every suggestion, but, but, but.

STIR STIR STIR

192

194

DELHI

Madam, today I am so happy. Everything is possible here! I just got my ration card! I'm happy! Nothing to worry about. From today, my existence is legal!

But... how did you get a ration card? Aren't you from Bangladesh?

Array madam, thanks to the fixers, everything is possible. Now I have no worries.

From today, my existence is legal! I have a ration card!

So why are you whispering?

You never know who is listening. I told you because I knew you'd understand, you know, both of us being Mussalmaan.

Hmmm. Yes, that bond.... How much did you pay the fixer?

Shh... don't ask.

198

But you just said, we've that Mussalmaan bond...

Tsk... tsk... never mind.

You know my husband was a real louse. He ran away a long time ago. Such is life. One has to find ways to move on.

So you live alone these days?

I board with someone. Pay him some money. He's a young fellow but he's a good, honest type.

Sab chalta hai. That's my feeling. Allah provides. A job is just a job. He will keep giving.

So have you been to Bangladesh anytime recently?

Earlier I used to go all the time. My mother is there, all my brothers and sisters... but now they have taken away my land. Rascals all. What is the use of going? I have nothing left there.

And now that I have my ration card, I don't have to worry anymore.

I have a Bangladeshi friend who has managed like this for years and I can tell you it's not easy.

Not in touch with her family, she lives alone shuttling from job to job.

I fear for Kanika.

It's just that things have become so difficult here.

The horror stories about girls being kidnapped...

God, I know. This is becoming a sick, bigoted society.

I remember when Paro's youngest daughter was on her deathbed, the doctor asked me...

HOW CAN YOU LET THESE HINDUS ENTER YOUR HOUSE AND TOUCH YOUR DISHES?

Uff... Paro, I don't know if there is an easy solution. Life's no magic there. It's not as if your son has tried to work hard despite all the opportunities he got here. I don't know if India is the solution but...

...

DELHI

You know I've had to stomach a lot of shit to be where I am now. Sometimes I felt disgusted having to stoop so low that I had to pretend to be someone else.

I can only barely imagine.

Remember that Bengali house I was working in? Once, during their festival, the landlady fell ill. So she asked me to make the preparations. I had no issue with her doing all that but I just didn't feel right about it....

TUP

THUP CHUP

I felt a little angry and a little sad that day; what did I accomplish?—just survival.

But you're the ultimate survivor! I don't know anyone quite like you.

I managed only to live.

TUP
TAPA TUP
TUP
THUP

202

SALMAN RASHID

is a Fellow at the Royal Geographical Society and the author of eight travel books. The only Pakistani to have seen the North Face of K2, he trekked in the shadow of this great mountain on its northern or Chinese side. His writings on explorations, history, and travel have appeared in almost all leading publications. Most of his writings are posted on his blog: http://odysseuslahori.blogspot.in

He is based in Lahore.

MOHIT SUNEJA

is trained in Applied Art from the College of Art, Delhi where he is presently teaching as Assistant Professor. He is a versatile artist and is proficient in various illustration styles and genres. As a freelancer he has worked with many leading advertising agencies, publishing houses, design houses, and independent authors. He is also involved with pre-production for animation and ad films. He enjoys travelling and photography, and loves to play his flute under the colourful clouds.

I TOO HAVE
SEEN LAHORE!

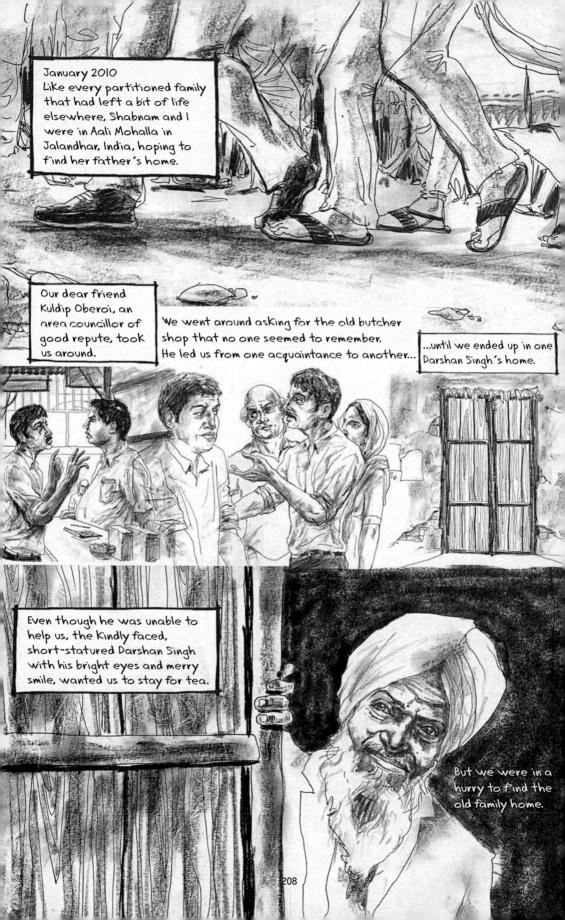

January 2010
Like every partitioned family that had left a bit of life elsewhere, Shabnam and I were in Aali Mohalla in Jalandhar, India, hoping to find her father's home.

Our dear friend Kuldip Oberoi, an area councillor of good repute, took us around.

We went around asking for the old butcher shop that no one seemed to remember. He led us from one acquaintance to another...

...until we ended up in one Darshan Singh's home.

Even though he was unable to help us, the kindly faced, short-statured Darshan Singh with his bright eyes and merry smile, wanted us to stay for tea.

But we were in a hurry to find the old family home.

As we were walking through Rainak Bazaar, Kuldip said someone wanted to speak with me.

There he was again, Darshan Singh, with his twinkling eyes and slow, shuffling gait.

He came up to me, took me by the elbow and said, 'I too have seen Lahore! I once went to the zoo there with my father and brothers.'

By now, I had encountered many such sentiments in India, and was in a hurry to catch up with the others in the crowded bazaar.

But the look in his eyes, the happiness in his smile and the emotion with which he had delivered that simple sentence stayed with me.

And so, on learning that the house we sought had been pulled down a few years ago, Shabnam and I decided to return to Darshan Singh's home.

If ever I have brought real happiness to anyone it has been to Darshan Singh, by the simple act of returning to talk to him.

His eyes twinkling, he did not tire of telling his family that we had returned especially to talk with him.

209

Darshan Singh was eight years old in 1947. He was born in village Klasswala near Pasrur where his family was comfortably well off. His father ran a thriving restaurant in Rawalpindi's Gwalmandi and the family lived in a rented house near the restaurant.

In 1944, Darshan joined Standard High School.

The young boy led a peaceful life, walking back and forth between home and school, running across the streets...

...the large pipal tree under which he and his mates played marbles...

210

Then one day, young Darshan's world exploded into flames—an event whose cause and meaning his young mind failed to fathom.

Word was that this part of Punjab would soon become Pakistan and non-Muslims would have to go across the Ravi to the east. This made no sense to the young mind of Darshan Singh. Klasswala was home, he had friends here—Muslim, Sikh, and Hindu.

Though their immediate locality was untroubled, they could see from the roof of their home, the eerie glow of fires raging in other areas.

Presently his father, Varyam Singh, announced that they were to leave Rawalpindi. Though he was unable to identify the reason, Darshan felt the fear in the air.

Everywhere, people were on the move, carrying tin trunks and cloth bags, kitchen supplies and bedrolls, leading cattle, supporting their elderly relatives, walking, walking, walking, ever eastward.

Sardars Satnam Singh and Gurdial Singh, influential Bajwa landlords of the village, organised army trucks to transport the Hindu and Sikh families of Klasswala to Pasrur railway station...

..for the journey across the new line drawn by history across the heart of an ancient land.

Darshan Singh remembers how when the train arrived it was crammed with people, with little room for anyone else to get in.

The women, children, and elderly were stuffed in the crowded cars, while the men rode on the roof.

The train was to go southeast from Pasrur, through Narowal and Jassar, across the magnificent steel spans of the bridge over the Ravi, and deposit its passengers at Dera Nanak.

Now the bridge at Jassar sits wholly in Pakistan, but its piers on the left bank of the Ravi tread the border between the two new countries that were to hate each other for decades to come.

And the locomotive driver, being a Muslim, refused to go into the country whose people were killing his co-religionists.

Meanwhile, outside the train in the drizzling August night, there stood a host of armed men.

If young Darshan Singh shared the terror that coursed through his co-passengers, he did not talk of it.

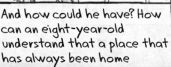
And how could he have? How can an eight-year-old understand that a place that has always been home

can suddenly turn into enemy territory, its people ready to kill their erstwhile neighbours.

Now, the Bajwas of Klasswala who were respected and well known in the area were also on the train, leaving the homes they had known for centuries.

The train stopped just short of the bridge and the men outside waited for the refugees to alight.

The noise was about killing the passengers to avenge the massacre of Muslims fleeing westward.

For the first time, Darshan Singh was truly terrified.

214

In that one instant something went very right.

Something inexplicably human took place—the inherent goodness that lives, even if in small measures, in all human beings, came to the fore.

The crowd of men, armed with guns, clubs, swords and farm implements, quieted down.

216

The men who would have murdered them as compensation for the deaths of Muslims elsewhere, now watched them leave.

Darshan Singh recalls that after crossing the Ravi the entire trainload of people sat down for no one knew where to go in the dark of the rainy night.

At daybreak, they found the riverbank and surrounding fields littered with hundreds of human corpses—the unfortunate Muslims whose cruel massacre these poor people had almost paid for with their own lives.

On the way to Dera Nanak and further to Batala, they saw the country similarly littered with the dead—the tragic harvest of partition.

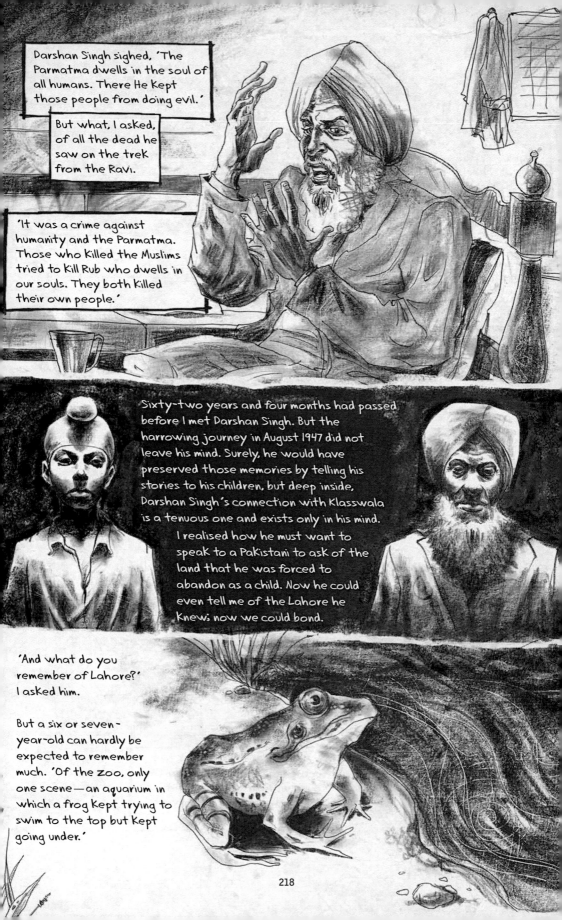

Darshan Singh sighed, 'The Parmatma dwells in the soul of all humans. There He kept those people from doing evil.'

But what, I asked, of all the dead he saw on the trek from the Ravi.

'It was a crime against humanity and the Parmatma. Those who killed the Muslims tried to kill Rub who dwells in our souls. They both killed their own people.'

Sixty-two years and four months had passed before I met Darshan Singh. But the harrowing journey in August 1947 did not leave his mind. Surely, he would have preserved those memories by telling his stories to his children, but deep inside, Darshan Singh's connection with Klasswala is a tenuous one and exists only in his mind.

I realised how he must want to speak to a Pakistani to ask of the land that he was forced to abandon as a child. Now he could even tell me of the Lahore he knew; now we could bond.

'And what do you remember of Lahore?' I asked him.

But a six or seven-year-old can hardly be expected to remember much. 'Of the zoo, only one scene—an aquarium in which a frog kept trying to swim to the top but kept going under.'

And Darshan Singh laughed like a child again. If ever I have done anything worthwhile in my life, it was this.

Back home, I drove to Klasswala to photograph the home that bore the names of Hukam Singh, Deva Singh and Varyam Singh, Darshan's grandfather, uncle and father, respectively.

But the house is gone. Gone too are the childhood friends of his memory.

When I return to Jalandhar, I will not have the promised photos of the double-storeyed house that Darshan Singh remembers in Klasswala.

end

MAHMUD RAHMAN

is a writer and translator. He came of age in Dhaka during
the upsurge of the late sixties that led to the creation of
Bangladesh. During the 1971 war, he was a refugee in Calcutta.
His first book, *Killing the Water: Stories,* was published in 2010,
and his second book, *Black Ice,* a translation of Mahmudul Haque's
novel *Kalo Borof* came out in 2012. He is still tinkering with his
first novel *The Fiction Factory* which is set in contemporary
Bangladesh and centred around themes of violence, image-making
and propaganda.

He lives in the San Francisco Bay Area.

PINAKI DE

is a graphic designer and illustrator who has done numerous
book covers for publishers like Penguin, HarperCollins, Hachette,
Random House, Westland, Rupa, Zubaan and others. He also has
a day job as a Professor of English Literature.
Presently, he is working on his first graphic novel based on Partition.

He lives in Chandannagar, a quiet suburb near Kolkata.

PROFIT & LOSS

As the Raj took its leave, and the white-crescent-on-green flag was hoisted in Dhaka...

... I was yet to be born.

The only family story I have heard of that day is that my Nana, mother's father, lit a cigarette.

He was not a smoker.

Lighting a cigarette can have different meanings.

Some smoke to calm their nerves.

Some light up after they make love.

For my grandfather, it was an act of celebration.

Both my father and grand-father marked Pakistan's birth by starting businesses....

PAK MOTORS

My father launched Pak Motors, a car dealership.

The name would later attach itself to the local bus stop, becoming today's Bangla Motors after 1971.

BANGLA MOTORS

My grandfather opened Azad Pharmacy. With the names they chose, both men appear to have welcomed Pakistan. My grandfather chose Azad (free in Urdu), a word popular at that time.

My father chose Pak, though not quite Pakistan. The opening of businesses by two Bengali Muslim middle-class men signalled that they, like others of their class, recognised in that moment an opportunity.

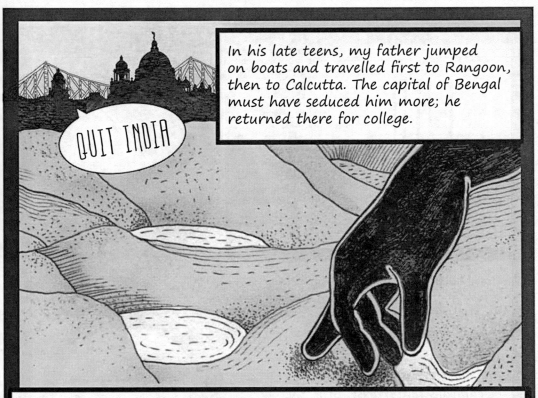

In his late teens, my father jumped on boats and travelled first to Rangoon, then to Calcutta. The capital of Bengal must have seduced him more; he returned there for college.

QUIT INDIA

He joined the Calcutta Police. In 1942, he quit and moved to Dhaka. Perhaps it was 'desher taan', the desire for the delta of his childhood. Or he might have felt the effects of churning in Calcutta: the pressures on the police from the Quit India movement and communal tensions swirling in the air.

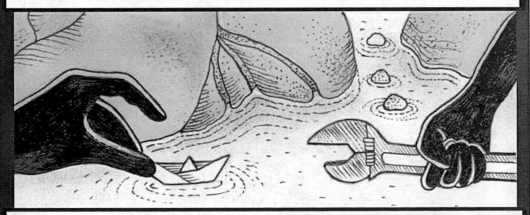

He alluded to resentments among colleagues. Meanwhile, his heart had found other attractions: designing boats, tinkering with cars, and a desire to try his hand at business.

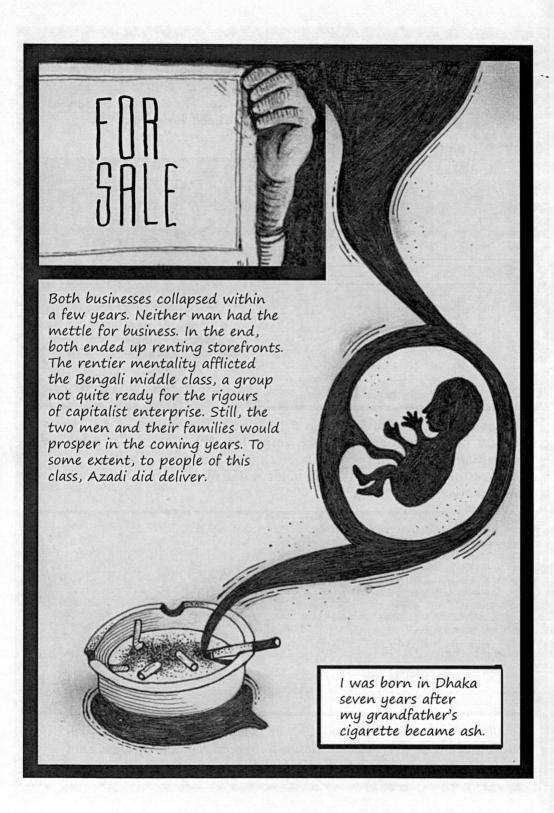

FOR SALE

Both businesses collapsed within a few years. Neither man had the mettle for business. In the end, both ended up renting storefronts. The rentier mentality afflicted the Bengali middle class, a group not quite ready for the rigours of capitalist enterprise. Still, the two men and their families would prosper in the coming years. To some extent, to people of this class, Azadi did deliver.

I was born in Dhaka seven years after my grandfather's cigarette became ash.

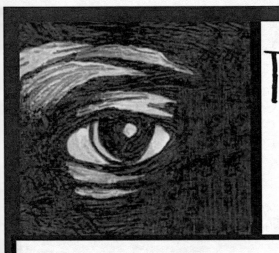

My hometown, in that first decade after 1947, saw a new mix. White men vacated positions of authority. Poorer migrants from Bihar now streamed in. The background to Partition was marked by distrust and hostility that exploded into unspeakable violence between Hindus and Muslims who had long lived side by side.

There would continue to be riots afterwards, big ones in 1950 and 1964. A vivid image from the second one stays in my mind: Hindu families running through our neighbourhood with mattresses on their heads.

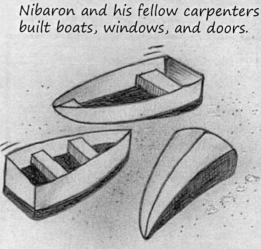

Nibaron and his fellow carpenters built boats, windows, and doors.

Yet our larger neighbourhood itself was mixed. Our first doctor was Horsho Babu.

The land where the Sonargaon Hotel stands today was home to a community of Hindu potters.

An Anglo-Indian lady, Mrs Ellis tutored me in English.

There was a cremation ghat across the road, along the khal that has now been filled up. It was probably during the 1964 riot that the Hindus left.

Today, the legacy
of 1947 we recall
most is that freedom
from the Raj brought
new shackles.

The groundwork was laid for another clash, this time a war, with
our Pakistani overlords. With the crackdown on 25 March 1971,
my oldest brother rebelled from within the army.
While he joined the Mukti Bahini,
I fled to Calcutta.

YOUR LANGUAGE

MUKTI JUDDHO

Even before my older brother's family arrived, I was welcomed by my bhabhi's (brother's wife) relatives into their Park Circus home. Though not as bad as the camps, life was difficult for most refugees who arrived in Calcutta. I recall the trials faced by my friends. Housing was scarce. Even when they found a room, there was no place to have a bath, but I was grateful that a family connection gave me a place to sleep, eat, shower, and enjoy new friendships.

Through them, and the neighbourhood...

the world of Calcutta and India opened up for me.

Calcutta was my first big city experience, and I was spoiled for life.

I was delighted to see women on the streets in a way that didn't exist in Dhaka back then. I don't know how we behaved, but the male gaze there didn't seem to have that starved edge that is still prevalent in Dhaka. In so many ways Calcutta was kind to us.

Though I would only stay there for six months, the city, once home to my father for sixteen years, became a sort of home to me. I have only visited it four times since the war, and yet, each time, I have found comfort there.

Perhaps another reason is that I fell in love there for the first time— though in typical Bengali fashion,

I never found the courage to voice it.

This should have been the last time that people here would be forced out in the name of religion. Unfortunately, it was not to be. To our shame, we could not guarantee security to the Hindus among us. The Pakistani Enemy Property Act would stay under a new name, there would be riots again and, with Islam declared the state religion, minorities would become second-class citizens. Confronted by those who swagger that this is Muslim Bangla, Hindus still feel pressured to leave.

With liberation in 1971, we undid the new chains imposed on us, removing one hateful legacy of 1947. When will we put behind us that other legacy of Partition: of people forced out of their homes carrying memories of neighbours turning on them in hate? It would help if we talked about it more. When the subcontinent's monsoon anniversary of that day just came by, we acted as if August 1947 only mattered to India and Pakistan, not to us.

How so far from the truth?

End

MALINI GUPTA

is a development worker by profession and a wanderer by choice.
She has been part of many exciting (and once in a while, not so exciting)
processes of change in social and economic structures, mainly in rural areas.

She has worked with government projects as well as non-governmental
initiatives through national and international development agencies.
While the bulk of her work is in India, she has also gathered relevant
experience in its neighbouring countries as well as East Africa.

She lives in her ancestral home in Delhi with her daughters and her dog
as a part of a rambling, eccentric and a Very-Bengali-Joint-Family. She is
forever planning to return to her place of birth.

DYUTI MITTAL

is an illustrator, graphic designer and comic book artist.
She graduated from Srishti School of Art, Design and
Technology, Bangalore, in Visual Communication Design
and explored the graphic novel medium first in 2009 with
a short graphic novel titled 'Flaw', initiated as her diploma
project.

She has since been freelancing, and also been a fellow with
Sarai CSDS, 2012. She works across mediums and hopes
to explore more styles of storytelling in the future
and infuse more relevance and beauty into her illustration
and writing.

She is currently based out of Delhi.

THE TABOO

1999, Ranaghat.
Bamboo. Paddy. Mango orchards.
The land looked rich and tranquil, presided over by deep grey monsoon clouds. But the people who lived on it were apparently neither rich nor tranquil. And unfortunately, it was the latter that brought me here.

It was a new job, in a new area. As a field officer in a microfinance programme, I was to work in the villages in this part of Nadia district, West Bengal, which in spite of a rich tradition of handicrafts, spirituality and the ability to grow three crops a year, was still one of West Bengal's poorest districts.

Cooper's Camp
Ranaghat
Nadia

My work was to provide technical support to women's savings and credit groups through a 'Samiti', or collective, based out of the village of Duttaphulia. So here I was, in my Mahindra jeep, heading towards Ranaghat, the nearest town. A journey I would make many, many times in the years to come. Thus, every day, I would drive into a hitherto unknown (and mostly unimagined) Bengal. I had grown up in neighbouring Chhotanagpur—close enough to fall in the shadow of Bengal's supposed emancipation yet far enough for the truth to remain hidden.

238

240

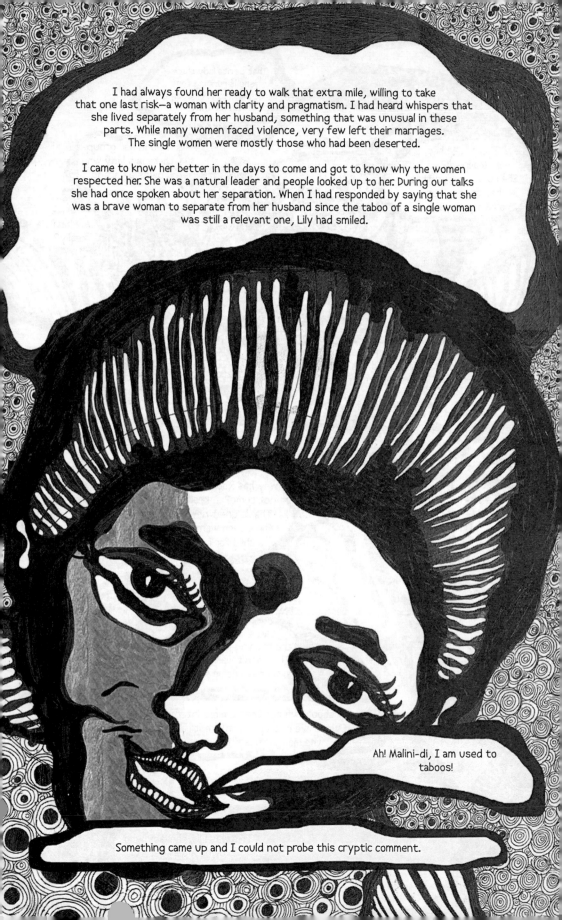

I had always found her ready to walk that extra mile, willing to take that one last risk—a woman with clarity and pragmatism. I had heard whispers that she lived separately from her husband, something that was unusual in these parts. While many women faced violence, very few left their marriages. The single women were mostly those who had been deserted.

I came to know her better in the days to come and got to know why the women respected her. She was a natural leader and people looked up to her. During our talks she had once spoken about her separation. When I had responded by saying that she was a brave woman to separate from her husband since the taboo of a single woman was still a relevant one, Lily had smiled.

Ah! Malini-di, I am used to taboos!

Something came up and I could not probe this cryptic comment.

Samar and I both grew up at Cooper's. We had the same dreams of a good life, a home. We both wanted to get out of this place. We got married and the first few years were great. But somewhere down the years, Samar stopped dreaming. He couldn't keep any job. He was ill-tempered and sullen, started drinking, then gambling. Thankfully we never had children—he would have made a terrible father. For him, I was the one who had ruined everything. I was always egging him on to do more. The writing on the wall was clear—he was just not interested. But like all women, I waited till my back was to the wall. One day, he raised his hand and I walked out. And I have no plans to return. But I do check on him once in a while. No hopes, Malini-di.

Leaving me with the thought of destinies and battlefields, Lily called out for her helper Nemai.

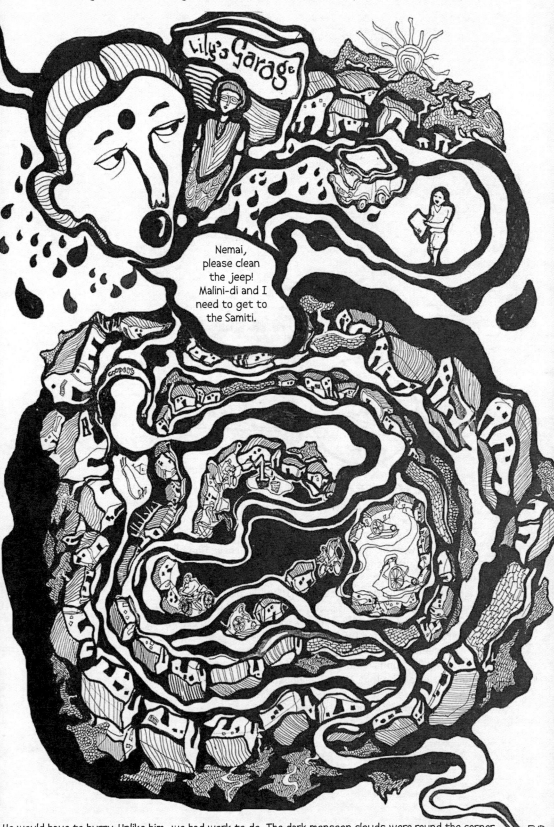

He would have to hurry. Unlike him, we had work to do. The dark monsoon clouds were round the corner. END.

MARIA M LITWA
is a freelance photographer and multimedia director.
At the end of 2011 she graduated in photography from
the University of Applied Sciences and Arts in Dortmund,
Germany, with the multimedia story 'Inside Geneva Camp',
shot in Dhaka, Bangladesh.

Her work has been exhibited internationally at renowned art
and photography festivals such as The New York Photo Awards,
Darmstädter Days of Photography, the International Festival
Sarajevo Winter and the Delhi Photo Festival.
The multimedia 'Inside Geneva Camp' was broadcast on
German TV and is featured in the *IM Magazine,* the online
magazine of The Inge Morath Foundation/Magnum Photos.

She is based in Cologne, Germany.

WELCOME TO
GENEVA CAMP

{Adapted from the original multimedia story 'Inside Geneva Camp'}

THE BIGGEST EXODUS IN HUMAN HISTORY CAME WITH THE PARTITION OF INDIA IN 1947. THE BLOODY CLASHES OF FAITHS, BELONGINGS, IDENTITIES, AND EVEN LANGUAGES MADE THE PARTITION AN ONGOING NARRATIVE. FEARING PERSECUTION AND DANGER IN INDIA BECAUSE OF THEIR RELIGION, THOUSANDS OF URDU-SPEAKING MUSLIMS FROM BIHAR AND OTHER STATES MOVED TO EAST PAKISTAN, TODAY'S BANGLADESH.

HOWEVER, AFTER THE PAKISTANI ARMY EVACUATED THE NEWBORN BANGLADESH IN 1971, THE BIHARIS WERE LEFT BEHIND. BENGALIS SAW THEM AS TRAITORS AND REFUSED TO ACCEPT THEM AS BANGLADESHIS BECAUSE THEY SPOKE URDU.

PAKISTAN TOO SAW NO REASON TO ACCEPT SUCH A LARGE NUMBER OF PEOPLE.

WELCOME TO GENEVA CAMP IN DHAKA. THIS IS THE LARGEST CAMP IN BANGLADESH, HOUSING ROUGHLY 25,000 PEOPLE IN AN AREA SPANNING THREE FOOTBALL FIELDS.

THEY CLAIMED THAT THEY DIDN'T SHARE MUCH WITH THE BIHARIS, CULTURALLY OR HISTORICALLY, OTHER THAN A COMMON LANGUAGE.

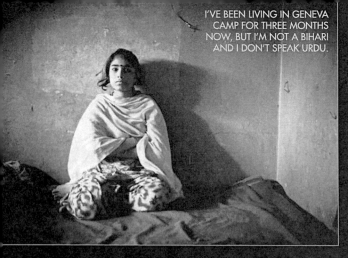

I'VE BEEN LIVING IN GENEVA CAMP FOR THREE MONTHS NOW, BUT I'M NOT A BIHARI AND I DON'T SPEAK URDU.

AFTER MY WEDDING MY MOTHER-IN-LAW BROUGHT ME HERE TO LIVE TOGETHER WITH MY HUSBAND'S FAMILY

DON'T GO TO SCHOOL ANYMORE ALTHOUGH I'D REALLY LIKE TO. MY HUSBAND'S FAMILY DOESN'T WANT ME TO GO, THEY CAN'T AFFORD TO SEND ME OR EVEN THEIR OWN CHILDREN TO SCHOOL. WE ARE A FAMILY OF 16 MEMBERS.

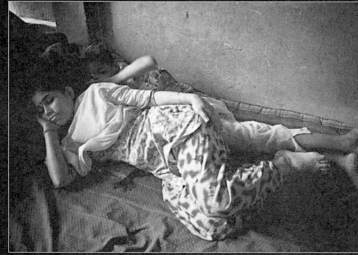

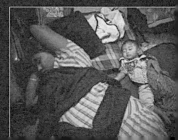

INSTEAD I HELP MY SISTERS-IN-LAW WITH THE HOUSEWORK LIKE WASHING AND CLEANING, BUT I NEVER COOK, BECAUSE I HAVEN'T LEARNED TO. MY MOTHER-IN-LAW ALWAYS REMINDS ME OF THAT.

I OFTEN FEEL LONELY HERE. I DON'T KNOW ANYONE, THERE'S NO FRIEND AROUND AND I PREFER TO STAY AT HOME AND WATCH TV TO GOING OUT.

SHABNAM, 20, STUDENT

NOBODY WANTS TO LIVE IN A PLACE LIKE THIS.

IT IS AWFULLY NOISY AND DIRTY AND YOU DON'T HAVE ANY PRIVACY HERE!

ONCE I COMPLETE MY STUDIES I WILL HAVE MUCH BETTER JOB OPPORTUNITIES AND I HOPE I CAN AFFORD TO MOVE OUT OF THE CAMP SOME DAY.

I HOPE I CAN EVENTUALLY GO TO PAKISTAN TO VISIT ALL MY RELATIVES. BUT I DON'T WANT TO LIVE THERE. MY LIFE IS HERE IN BANGLADESH.

PUTUL, 24, TEACHER

FOR THE LAST FOUR MONTHS I HAVEN'T BEEN PAID MY SALARY. THE FUNDING FOR THE SCHOOL PROJECT HAS STOPPED.

I'M A TEACHER IN THE CAMP'S PRESCHOOL AND BESIDES TEACHING THE BASICS IN ALL SUBJECTS IT IS MY RESPONSIBLITY TO PREPARE THE CHILDREN FOR THE PUBLIC SCHOOLS THAT THEY WILL HOPEFULLY ATTEND AFTERWARDS.

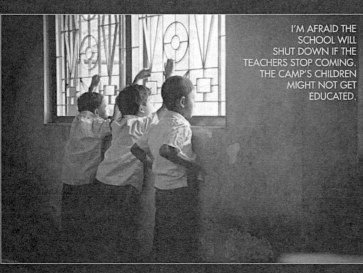

I'M AFRAID THE SCHOOL WILL SHUT DOWN IF THE TEACHERS STOP COMING. THE CAMP'S CHILDREN MIGHT NOT GET EDUCATED.

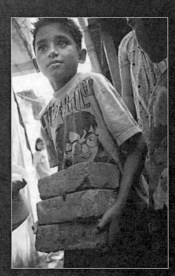

THE URDU-SPEAKING COMMUNITY HAS REMAINED STATELESS FOR 37 YEARS. AN ESTIMATED 250,000 SO-CALLED BIHARIS LIVE IN 116 GHETTO-LIKE SETTLEMENTS SPREAD ALL OVER BANGLADESH. IN 2008, THEY WERE FINALLY ALLOWED TO APPLY FOR THE NATIONAL ID CARD OF BANGLADESH.

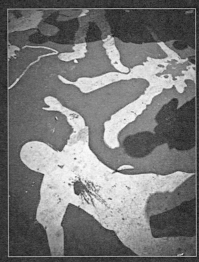

HOWEVER, MANY OF THEM, WHILE 'SETTLED' IN BANGLADESH, STILL FEEL LIKE A NOWHERE LOT INSIDE THEIR HEADS.

End

SYEDA FARHANA

was born in 1972 in Khulna, Bangladesh.
After studying social sciences, she went to Hamburg
to work on film production. Moved by a western artist's
work, she joined a diploma course in photojournalism in Dhaka.
Since then she has been exploring visual media both in art
and documentary form. She has authored visual and scholarly
projects on the Partition, migration and cities in South Asia
(documentary photo stories, art exhibitions, films, articles,
websites). Her works have been exhibited and awarded
in Bangladesh as well as abroad.

She lives in Dhaka and Chittagong.

NITESH MOHANTY

is a graphic designer and illustrator. He loves dabbling in
various forms of art in pursuit of telling a story. He has been
designing book covers for over a decade for various Indian
publishers such as Penguin, Picador, HarperCollins and others.

He is currently working on his first documentary film and can
be found loitering around with his camera. He's also writing
a book of poetry, thoughts, observations, scribbles and sketches.

He lives and works in Bombay.

LITTLE WOMEN

{Translated from Bengali by Bhaswati Ghosh}

I want to be a Tree

Tara, the star in Bengali, never came from the skies above...

My father grew up in Patna (India) with his sister.

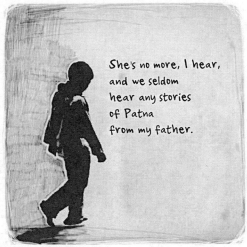

She's no more, I hear, and we seldom hear any stories of Patna from my father.

In those days, the British had set up an office for the Bengal-Bihar Railways in Pahartoli, Chittagong. As a driver with the Railways,

it is here that my father built a nest for his youth, old age and his last sleep.

In the daily whirlwind of survival, one never had the time to ask him, is this your real home?

Is this your country?

But it is here that I close my eyes

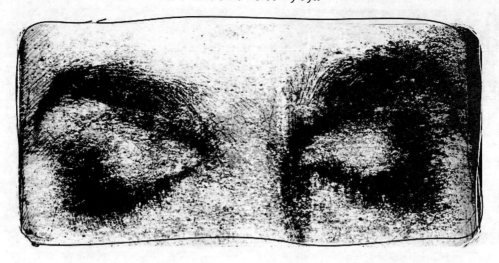

and see myself

as an actor on a stage

with my little sister

dancing next to me.

With my eyes open, I find myself
in this refugee camp, engrossed
in a daily struggle for survival.

But I know within myself, I will never leave acting, never.
I will educate my sister to go further ahead than I ever could.

A few years after the Liberation War of 1971,

my elder sister and her husband, along with many others, left this camp

and took the boat for a better life, from Koronofulli to a place called Orangi.

A group photo was taken before their departure. We were supposed to follow.

But that boat never arrived, we never departed.

We haven't heard from my sister ever since.
Who knows if they're alive or dead?
In his last days, father would often want to see her but....

Anyway,
these are just stories for me.
Only stories.
I have no past and
don't know if there's any future ahead.
I know I have a present.

If I close my eyes, I can see my roots entering the soil, this land I stand on.

I shall not look up at the birds; their wings don't impress me.
Today in this camp I live, I see many Bihari birds selling
pff their huts to the Bengali ones, in hushed tones of course.
In those 9 months of that war, so much happened here in Pahartoli.
Anarchy, bloodshed, land grabbing. After the war,
the Red Cross gave these camps to the Biharis.

This is history now but today these camps look like cages,
where I don't want to live. I can feel my roots

spreading and finding a home in the soil.
This is my land too and
all I want to be is a Tree.

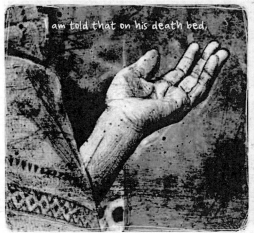

I am told that on his death bed,

my father often called for me—

"SHATI, SHATI, SHATI..."

However, Ma never did. My mother passed on with her vague sense of vanity.

When my grandfather finally closed his spice shop, Akbar, our neighbour pointed out how 'a family that stayed together in 1947, now breaks apart in 1992 with the breaking of the Babri Masjid in India'.

He was right.
Slowly our relatives
started leaving
Chittagong.
Baba too left with them,
with my elder sister.
My brother and I
stayed back with Ma.
I often wonder,
why did Ma stay back?

Last night, those birds
came in my dream again.
We flew together
for the day
and they asked me
the same thing again:
'Want to come with us?
Won't you?'

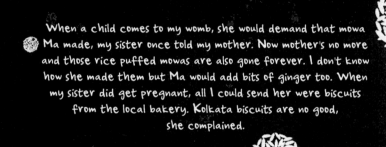

When a child comes to my womb, she would demand that mowa
Ma made, my sister once told my mother. Now mother's no more
and those rice puffed mowas are also gone forever. I don't know
how she made them but Ma would add bits of ginger too. When
my sister did get pregnant, all I could send her were biscuits
from the local bakery. Kolkata biscuits are no good,
she complained.

Every time we speak,
my sister cries,
pleads me to cross over.

Every time we speak,
I wonder what held my
mother back.

Why did I never ask Ma
while she was alive ?

Now my aunt's family might be leaving too. Recently they sold their house to some Barua, a Buddhist family.

They thought it was a secret till the local goons got a whiff and demanded their pound of flesh from the sales.

It's not getting any easier.

All my relatives get more curious by the day about my plans.

Why am I not leaving for India, they wonder.

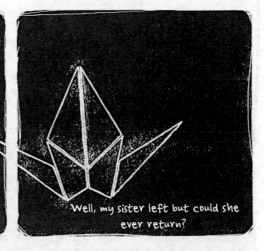

Well, my sister left but could she ever return?

It's like a one-way journey, forever.

But why should I?

Because I will get married there, for there are more and better Hindus on that side?

Will I get a job there with my degree from this side?

Here I live on my terms with my own money.
Will I be able to work there or
get sucked into domestic chores?
Or will I end up like Sandhya di,
as a sales girl in a sari shop?
Why did I attend university then....

Every time those birds come calling for me I try shooing them
away. But they return soon and leave me wondering

'Should I leave, Shouldn't I
' Should I? Shouldn't I?
houldn't I?   Should I?
Shoul   Should I? Shouldn't I?
Shoul   Shouldn't I?
Should I?   Shouldn't I?
Shouldn't I?   Shouldn't I?
Shouldn't I?   Shouldn't I?
Shouldn't I?

Should I?
Should I?

At this point, this thought looks like a rudderless journey inside my head.

End

273

PRIYA SEN

works with video and sound narratives as an artist, editor and sound designer, and occasionally teaches experimental film and practices.

She is currently based in New Delhi.

DEEWANA

Always on the move, Kanhaiya Lal Prem Deewana is a consultant to the Ministry of Love & Harmony in the three neighbouring countries.
He somehow manages to live a second life as a visual artist in Amritsar.

THE LAST CIRCUS

Parade Ground, Bangalore, 2012.

His name is Dasharath and he dreams of his brothers.

I prefer 'The Punjab' for North India.

Around sixty-six years ago he came here quite by chance.

[Although there must be something more powerful than chance; suffice it to say for now, it seemed like an act of destiny.]

His real name is
Don Emanuelle Stanislav
and his family is from Manila.
He was born in a circus in Lahore.

[He didn't say enough about how they got there and how he left, and sixty-six years later it doesn't seem that important.]

They told him that when he was born, Lal, the lion broke open his cage, came to have a look at him and was never seen again.

{And then, the circus was Partitioned.}

They were all trapeze artists, him and his brothers, and in 1947 he was the one to leave.

His father, who had an American passport, died in Calcutta.

Dasharath crossed the new border on an
elephant, and the Bengali Dog-Master
cried because he had to leave
his dogs behind.

On the previous night, the bulldog
had run into the Parrot-Trainer,
who then lost his balance and fell.
He was the drunkest of them all,
which is why he is still in Lahore.

The owner of this
circus is generous.
He owns four
circuses and a hotel
in South India.
The previous owner
wasn't destined
for such riches.

Dasharath left that circus
the day the owner died and
the new circus fell apart.

Don Emanuelle Stanislav watched
the horses slowly ride up the mountainside,
carrying great loads on their backs.
Beyond the mountains was a vast desert
plateau where no trees grew.
The horses won't make it, he thought,
they aren't meant for such distances.
Their whole world was a circus ring.
And what a ring it was!

EXEMPTED FROM
POLICE REPORTING

He called out to Jaanu—he found himself
screaming because he couldn't see her.
She was made of air that girl,
she could do anything on those horses!
She found her most perfect balance
as they rode around the ring in whirls
of dust and glitter.
But Jaanu was gone.
Forty years later, he wakes up
with her name on his lips.

Imagine seventy trucks on the Bangalore–Mysore Road, all in one line!
Packed with pelicans and tents and trapeze artists and dog and parrot-trainers;
drunks and clowns and fire-eaters and African, Nepalese and Russian artists
with or without the right papers; a kitchen for four hundred people, a man
from Manila, a journey made over sixty years ago! Dasharath travels on the
twenty-seventh truck with the two Nepalese trapeze artists—Mister Pavan and
Mister Deepak. They are talented and stylish and speak less than the others.

The pelicans are
inseparable.
They go
everywhere
together.

Don Emanuelle Stanislav dreams
of his brothers now and then.

They must still be the closing act—the most
phenomenal, most agile, magical flying duo,
who at the end of the show, would let
themselves fall as the audience cheered and wept
because they knew the grand old circus
was moving somewhere else the next day,
to a faraway city in a not-so-faraway country.

Tomorrow we leave for Shimoga. Finally.

DEPARTURE

SANJOY CHAKRABORTY

is a painter, performance artist, art writer and illustrator.
He completed his graduation from Rabindra Bharati University,
Kolkata. In his academic years he participated in many exhibitions
all over India. He also attended a student residency in *'Periphery 1.0'*,
Guwahati, in 2008. After returning to Bangladesh, he organised
an International Art Exhibition where young artists from India and
Bangladesh participated. Many of his articles on art have been published
in India and Bangladesh. He works full-time as a Lecturer at the
University of Dhaka and teaches part-time at Pathshala, South Asian Media
Institute, Dhaka.

BHASWATI GHOSH

writes and translates works of fiction and non-fiction. In 2009, she was granted
the Charles Wallace (India) Trust Fellowship for her Bengali-to-English
translation of *My Days with Ramkinkar Baij* (Niyogi, 2012). Her stories have
appeared in *Letters to My Mother* and *My Teacher is My Hero*, anthologies of
true stories published by Adams Media.

With a background in journalism, she has contributed to several websites
(including Stealing Time, Open Road Review, Humanities Underground,
Parabaas, Asia Writes), magazines (*Teenage Buzz, ByLine, Cause and Effect*)
and major Indian dailies (including *The Times of India, The Statesman* and
The Pioneer).

AN AFTERLIFE

{Translated from Bengali by Bhaswati Ghosh}

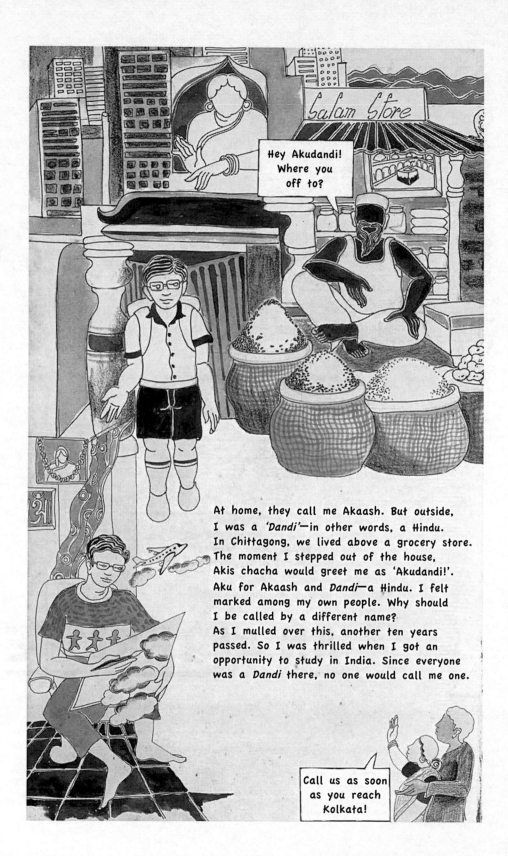

At home, they call me Akaash. But outside,
I was a *'Dandi'*—in other words, a Hindu.
In Chittagong, we lived above a grocery store.
The moment I stepped out of the house,
Akis chacha would greet me as 'Akudandi!'.
Aku for Akaash and *Dandi*—a Hindu. I felt
marked among my own people. Why should
I be called by a different name?
As I mulled over this, another ten years
passed. So I was thrilled when I got an
opportunity to study in India. Since everyone
was a *Dandi* there, no one would call me one.

Meeting Madhu meant a fresh lease of life for me. It was she who explained to me the differences between a *Bangaal* and a *Ghoti* (someone from West Bengal). I was told that serious conflict between the two escalated after Partition and continues to this day. This tension is evident in the competition between their popular soccer teams, Mohun Bagan of the *Ghoti* lot, and East Bengal of the *Bangaal* set.

Soon, I started visiting her home, where I was pampered
to no end. One of the obvious reasons was that I was
from Chittagong. Madhu's grandparents would demand more
and more of the latest Chittagong stories while I heard
so many histories of the town I came from.

Over tea and snacks, our conversations brought alive
so many Chittagongs and every evening, we parted with
the realisation that their Chittagong and mine were
forever different but also the same.

My two-year Master's course was drawing to a close. Swamped with examinations and submissions, I didn't realise my two years in Kolkata were nearly over.

As I prepared to leave Kolkata after my exams, Madhu and I felt keenly the depth of our bond. As the only child of my parents, it was impossible for me to settle in Kolkata. On the other side, her parents, having left Bangladesh, couldn't think of sending Madhu there. Even if it was Chittagong.

On my last evening in Kolkata, the two of us sat
on the banks of the Ganges for a long time.
As we sat still and silent, the evening was closing
in and so was everything around.

It's been two years since I left Kolkata. Madhu is still there. A common friend tells me she's married and happy. Neither of us tried keeping in touch and I don't know why. Perhaps it was meant to be that way. Yet there are times when I feel ours might have been a different story had the borders not come up. Anyway....

SANJOY CHAKRABORTY
Lecturer,
Dept. of Fine Arts,
University of Dhaka

Bailey Road.
How much?
Please! This is
Dhaka, not
Kolkata!

END

MEHREEN MURTAZA

began crafting a new invention in 1986, accidentally stumbling upon
the discovery of the Mentalex—a machine that uses the power of light
to bring supra natural powers to the user's mind. It is in fact a strange
artefact of unknown origin, discovered during a balneo therapy
session. Essentially, a scientific study about the interaction between
the angle of the rain, the shapes of the drops and the probability of
being happy led to this innovative breakthrough. In the midst of taking
out a patent on this discovery (in the hope that this would solve the
planet's geopolitical problems), Murtaza began to emanate luminous
laser beams from her cerebral cortex.

She is currently designing the first quantum space probe that will allow
time travel through high-resolution mapping of the human brain epigenome.
On this planet, Mehreen Murtaza has been occasionally spotted in Lahore,
and is represented by Grey Noise, Dubai and Experimenter, Kolkata.

Her current whereabouts are unknown.

BASTARDS OF
UTOPIA

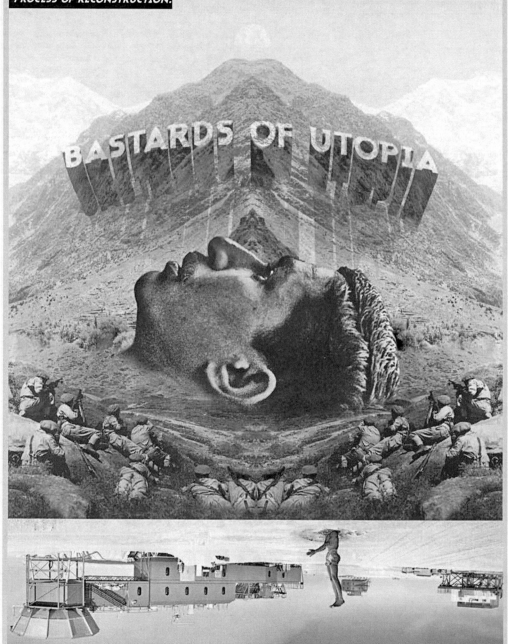

BASTARDS OF UTOPIA

AS ABOVE, SO BELOW

294

'I KNOW THAT ALL IS NOT RIGHT IN MY HEAD...'

HE WAS NOT MENTALLY SOUND AND WAS UNDER TREATMENT FOR OVER 65 YEARS. HE WAS INTELLIGENT AND PHILOSOPHICAL, BUT HE WAS ABNORMAL. NUMEROUS SUCH DISORDERS PRODUCE A DIFFUSE LOSS OF BRAIN FUNCTION ACROSS THE CORTEX AND WITHIN MULTIPLE SUBCORTICAL STRUCTURES.

WHEN WE WERE BORN, OUR MOTHER WANTED AN OPERATION DONE TO SPLICE US APART...

BUT THE DOCTORS SAID...

'CAN'T BE DONE AS THEY SHARE TOO MANY OF THE SAME VITAL ORGANS, AND IF THEY ARE SEPARATED, THEY'LL DIE.'

'THE IRREGULAR WORLD ORDER AROSE FROM AN ILL-FATED NERVE CONNECTION ESTABLISHED BETWEEN GOD AND A MEMBER OF MY FAMILY IN THE PAST.'

'GOD COULD NOT SUSPEND THE NERVE CONNECTION IN TIME BECAUSE I WAS MISUSING IT TO FORM A CONSPIRACY IN THE FRONT COURTS OF HEAVEN. THE CONSPIRACY WAS AIMED AT FIGHTING A WAR AGAINST MY OWN FAMILY BY DENYING IT OFFSPRING.'

'THE WILFUL MISUSE OF A NERVE CONNECTION FOR THE PURPOSE OF HARMING ANOTHER PERSON AND MANIPULATING HIS MIND IS KNOWN AS SOUL MURDER. IN AN EFFORT TO RESTORE THE WORLD ORDER, GOD HAS SUBJECTED ME TO A PROCESS OF EMASCULATION AND SUBSEQUENTLY TO THE PROCREATION OF A NEW HUMAN BREED.'

'IN THIS PROCESS, THE HUMAN SOULS CONCERNED WERE CALLED TO A NEW HUMAN LIFE ON OTHER PLANETS, PRESUMABLY BY BEING BORN IN THE MANNER OF A HUMAN BEING, PERHAPS RETAINING SOME DIM MEMORY OF THEIR EARLIER EXISTENCE....'

TEXT APPROPRIATED FROM MEMOIRS OF MY NERVOUS ILLNESS, BY DANIEL SCHREBER, 1903

End

RABBI SHERGILL

is an Indian musician famous for his debut album
Rabbi and the chart-topper song of 2005, 'Bulla Ki Jaana'.
His music has been described variously as Rock, Sufiana,
and 'semi-Sufi, semi-folksy kind of music with a lot of
Western arrangements'. Rabbi has been called
'Punjabi music's true urban balladeer'.

His songs are deeply philosophical and blend archaic,
almost lost, Punjabi phrases into far more recent
Indian rock music with great ease. Rabbi's music has
been inspired by Rock, Hard Rock as well as Sufi and
Punjabi folk music. His favourite musicians include
Bruce Springsteen, Led Zeppelin, Aerosmith and
Jimmy Page.

VISHWAJYOTI GHOSH

is a cartoonist-graphic novelist, known for
his cribs and rants on social media.

He lives and works in New Delhi.

CABARET WEIMAR

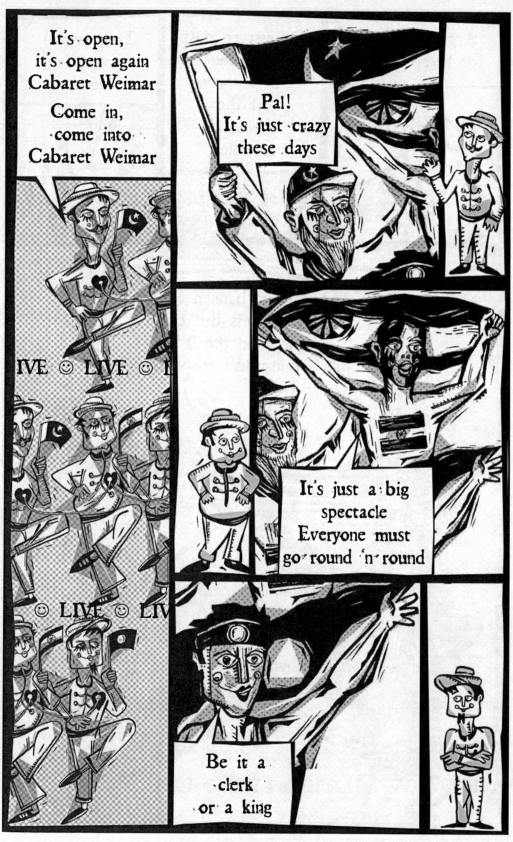

305

End

BEENA SARWAR

is a journalist, artist and documentary filmmaker focusing
on media, gender, peace and human rights issues, working with
television and print media in Pakistan and abroad.
She is a founding member of the Pakistan India Peoples Forum
for Peace and Democracy (PIPFPD) formed in 1994.
Since January 2010, she has been working as Editor for
Aman ki Asha (www.amankiasha.com), a peace initiative between
the Jang Group of Newspapers, Pakistan and *The Times of India*.
She blogs at Journeys to Democracy (www.beenasarwar.wordpress.com),
and is on Twitter @beenasarwar.

PRASANNA DHANDARPHALE

is an illustrator and artist who likes experimenting with different styles.
He has won several awards including Best Press Illustration two years on the trot.
He has also illustrated a graphic novel published by Penguin India.
By profession he is a character designer and pre-production artist, working in
the animation and art industry since 2001. He was the Character Dept head for
two animated feature films and several TV series. His work in the 2007 animated
film *Dashavatar* earned him nominations for Best Character Design.
Those who want original Prasanna Dhandarphale art, meet him over coffee.
By the end of the meeting, most of the paper napkins on your table will have drawings
of the most interesting people in the coffee shop.

Prasanna lives and works in Pune.

MILNE DO!

So here we are,
two neighbours. Same people.
We share a history and general culture.
We love the same music, the same food,
the same films. When we meet in
a third country, we become best friends,
burying our same differences.
But in our own neck of the woods we
could be aliens at opposite ends of the
world, 'othering' the other side.
The hawk eyes ensure the lack of
interaction between the peoples.
Not because the people don't want
it but because the visas are
difficult to get.
But then, even with such difficulties,
come opportunities.

And a day later...

Hey Amit, would you like to write for my paper? I head the weekly magazine section, it's called 'The News on Friday'.

Oh wow, really?

It would be great. No Pakistani paper has any Indian writing for it. There hasn't been one at least since the 1965 war. It will be a great way to give our readers an insight into India.

That will be amazing. I would just love to...

Maybe a fortnightly 'Letter from Delhi'? I'm not sure how we'll manage to pay you because there are so many restrictions but we'll figure something out.

That's fine, Beena, More importantly...

I will have readers that side too! Done!

Today there are several Indian and Pakistani journalists reporting and writing for each other's newspapers and TV channels.
The Internet has broken barriers.
There are dozens of India-Pakistan initiatives, many spawned by initial meetings that took place at PIPFPD conventions.

But both countries still only allow two journalists each to be stationed across the border, based in the capital city—which they are not allowed to leave without special permission.
People still find it difficult to get visas to visit each other.

REPORTING LIVE FROM...

A spiritual or a cricket visa. Which is easier?

The most difficult is a Normal Visa!

Yes, Pakistan and India are inching towards normalising relations.
But for the people who are eager to meet...

...especially for divided families, it's an agonisingly slow process.
So please...

MILNE DO! Good things happen when we meet!

End

CYBERMOHALLA ENSEMBLE

is a constellation of Delhi-based writers and practitioners, that came together in 2009 and dissolved in May 2013. The ensemble made books, set up temporary structures for gatherings and conversations, created art works and designed a building.
Its members were **Azra Tabassum, Shamsher Ali, Neelofar, Lakhmi Kohli, Jaanu Nagar, Rabiya Qureshi, Love Anand, Babli Rai, Nasreen and Rakesh Khairalia.**

Their writings about Delhi are included in *Bahurupiya Shehr* (Rajkamal Prakashan) and in *Trickster City* (Penguin India). Their book *No Apologies for the Interruption* on cultural collisions produced around the culture of copy was published in 2011 by Sarai-CSDS, Delhi. *Everything Else is Ordinary,* a text that creates an imagined life of the mind of a worker was part of *Strikes at Time,* a video essay by Raqs Media Collective (2011). In 2006 members of the ensemble contributed to the blog, Nangla's Delhi (nangla.freeflux.net). In 2012, a 1:1 prototype of the building, the Cybermohalla Hub, which the ensemble formulated with architects Nikolaus Hirsch and Michel Mueller, was part of 'Sarai Reader 09: The Exhibition' (Devi Art Foundation, Gurgaon).
The ensemble also released the book *Cybermohalla Hub* (Sternberg/Berlin and Sarai-CSDS/Delhi), co-written with artists, philosophers, urbanists and poets from around the world, during the exhibition and ran their Bureau of Contemporary Jobs from inside the building (2012–13).

AMITABH KUMAR

is a designer/artist based between New Delhi and Bangalore. He graduated from the Faculty of Fine Arts, MSU Baroda and worked as part of the Sarai Media Lab (2006–10) where he researched and made comics, programmed events, designed books and co-curated an experimental art space. He is visiting faculty to the Srishti School of Art and Design and Technology, Bangalore, and is an initiating member of the comics ensemble, the Pao Collective.

MAKE IT
YOUR OWN

{Translated from Hindi by Shveta Sarda}

This bundle has never been
opened. It has been passed
from generation to generation.
It is yours now. Don't ever undo
its knot.

Towards the north, a hundred
kilometres from here, there is
a night shelter. It has a door
at its entrance. Let the door
remain there.

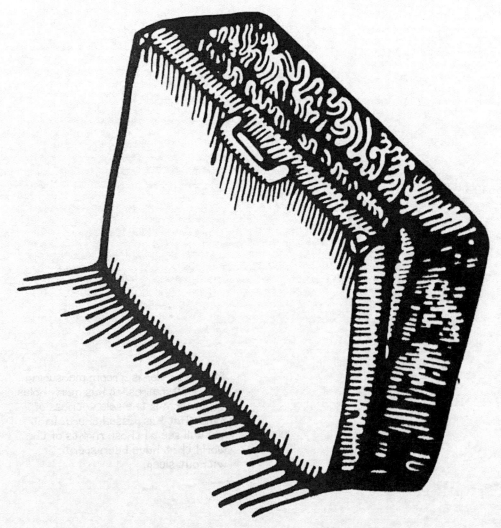

At the border is a room measuring 10-by-20 metres. It has many holes. That room is the sole witness of time that has passed there. In it you will see all those nights of the world that have been spent without sleep.

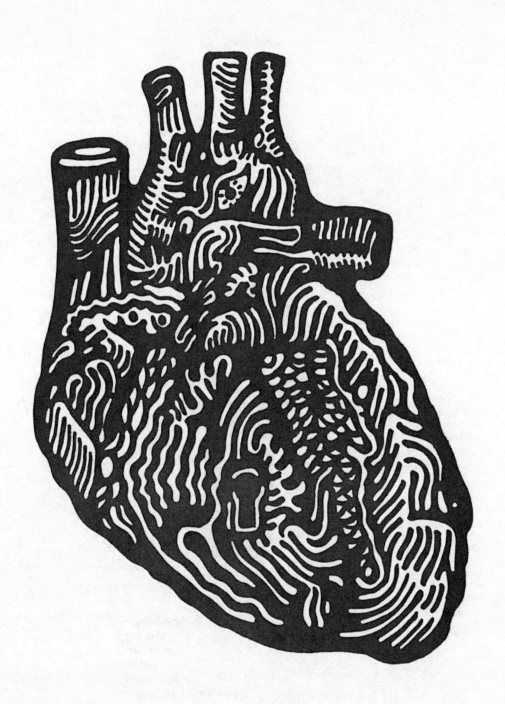

Everything—
　　the sky,
　the ocean,
　　　paths,
　distances,
caravans of strangers
—make everything your own.

make it
your own

End

ORIJIT SEN

is a graphic artist and designer based in New Delhi. He trained at the
National Institute of Design, Ahmedabad. He has helped conceptualise,
design and execute several exhibition and museum design projects,
including the India Pavilion at the World Expo 2005 in Aichi, Japan and
the Virasat-e-Khalsa Museum in Anandpur Sahib, Punjab.

Orijit also works with graphic narrative forms. His pioneering graphic novel
The River of Stories was published in 1994. He is one of the founders of the
Pao Collective—a group of comics artists and graphic novelists in Delhi, and
collaborated on the critically acclaimed *Pao Anthology of Comics* published
by Penguin.

In 1990, he co-founded People Tree, a centre for design, crafts and sustainable
living, which has grown to become a celebrated and unique cultural space in Delhi.
He heads the People Tree in-house design studio.

Making Faces

Nationality, Religion, Ethnicity, Gender, Race
and other Indisciplines in South Asia

by Dr Sen

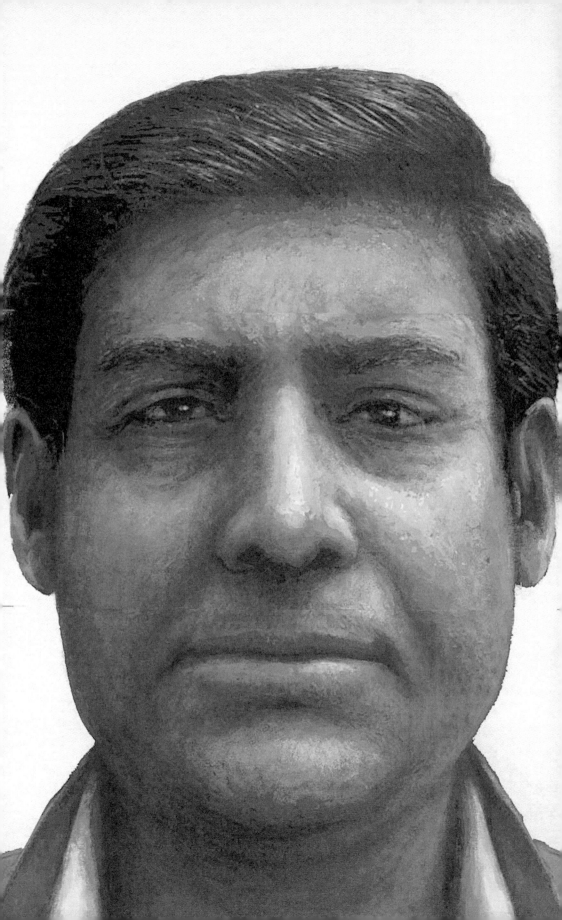

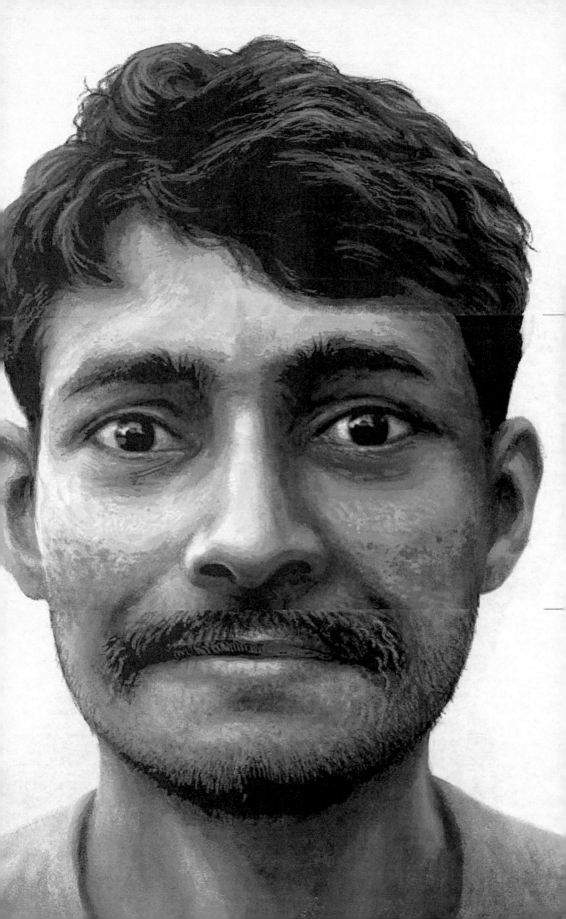

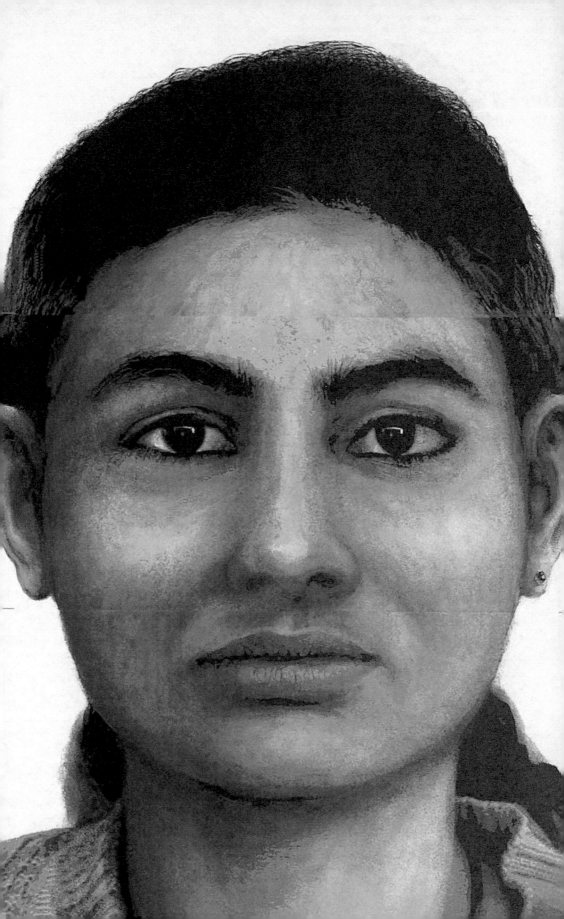

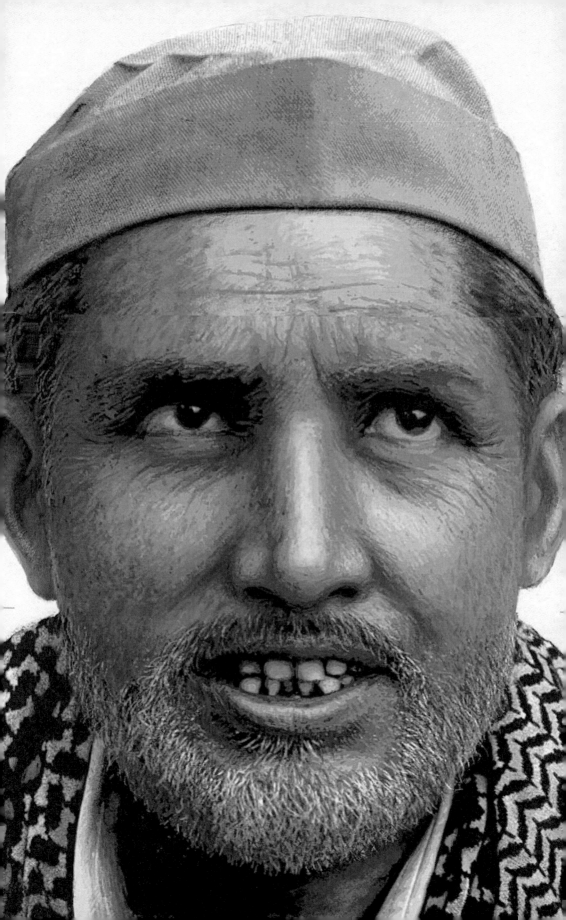

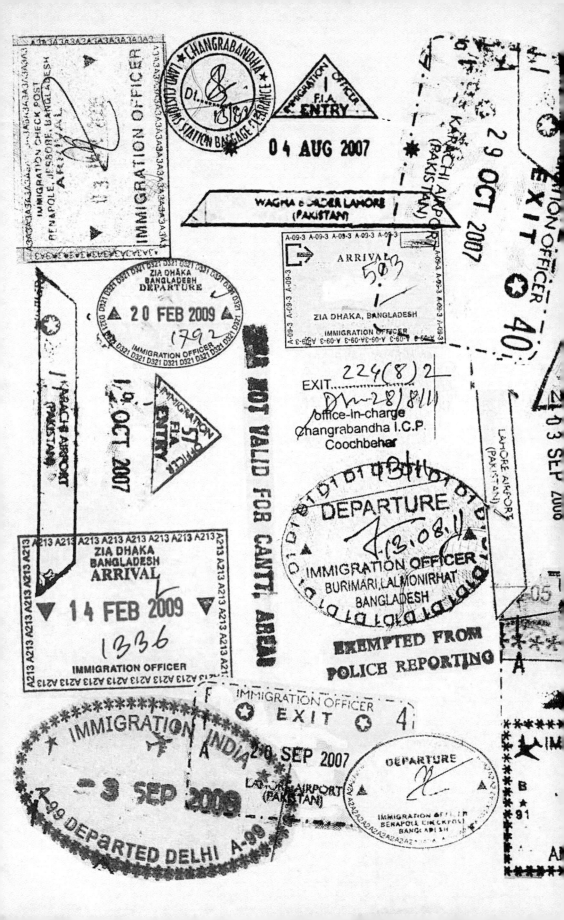